The BBC presents
the 102nd Season
of Henry Wood
Promenade
Concerts

Royal Albert Hall

19 July to
14 September 1996

Published by:
BBC Radio 3 Publications.
Editorial Office:
Room 815, Henry Wood
House, 3-6 Langham Place,
London W1A 1AA.

Distributed by BBC Books, a
division of BBC Worldwide,
80 Wood Lane,
London W12 0TT

© BBC 1996
ISBN 0 563 38753 X
Design: Ideology, London
Cover Illustration: Cathie Felstead
at The Organisation, London
Advertising: Hugh Muirhead
Printed by Taylor Bloxham Limited,
Leicester
Silverblade Matt 115gsm, Silverblade
Artboard 240gsm from MoDo Paper and
Metaphor cream 100gsm from Paperback

BBC ALEX VON KOETTLITZ THE IMAGE BANK

Contents

Don't miss
your free
CD in back
cover!

Introduction

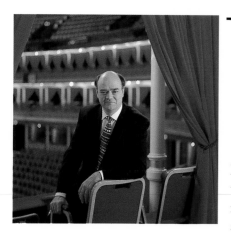

WELCOME TO THE SECOND century of the BBC Proms, and to a season we hope will be as crowded with musical adventure and stimulation as any of those that preceded it.

It is a special pleasure to welcome back Claudio Abbado and the Berlin Philharmonic, the Chicago Symphony under music directors past and present Georg Solti and Daniel Barenboim, the New York Philharmonic for the first time with their Music Director Kurt Masur, regular Prom favourites such as Mariss Jansons and the Oslo Philharmonic, and lively new visitors including Mikhail Pletnev's Russian National Orchestra and Frans Brüggen's Orchestra of the Eighteenth Century.

There are more concerts than ever: 72, plus a new linked chamber music series; a special Junior Prom as well as a Family Prom, and a day with three concerts all devoted to the music of a single composer, Igor Stravinsky. Not all anniversaries matter, but a quarter of a century since his death is worth marking, for he casts his shadow over all the music of our time. The magisterial symphonies of Bruckner in his centenary year are perfectly suited to the Royal Albert Hall, where he played the organ. So too the happy conjunction of the centenary of Roberto Gerhard and the fiftieth anniversary of the death of Manuel de Falla gives an opportunity to introduce to the Proms two of their major works. Haydn, on the other hand, is there simply for his neglected greatness: from his *Creation* on the First Night to the *Te Deum* on the Last, he will link the themes of the season in celebrating the creation and re-creation of music.

Our commitment to the new is as strong as ever, with a wide range of Prom premieres from Michael Tippett's last orchestral work, and one of Berthold Goldschmidt's earliest, to violin concertos by John Adams and Nicholas Maw, the seventy-year-old Hans Werner Henze's most recent piece for orchestra and Peter Maxwell Davies's latest symphony. There is an international

Left
Nicholas Kenyon,
Controller,
BBC Radio 3

Right
Previous Directors of the
Proms: from left,
Sir William Glock,
Sir John Drummond and
Robert Ponsonby

Director
Nicholas Kenyon,
Controller, BBC Radio 3
Assistant
Yvette Pusey

Administrator
Stephen Maddock
Secretary
Ceri Hunter

Marketing Manager
Judy Grahame
Publicity Officer
Leonora Thomson
Secretaries
Eve Saunders and
Judith Jerome

Publications Editor
George Hall
Publications Organiser
Karen Cardy
Assistant Editor
Matías Tarnopolsky
Publications Officer
Katina Dawe
Secretary
Edward Bhesania

group of BBC commissions from James Dillon, Detlev Glanert, Dominic Muldowney, Kevin Volans and John Woolrich, all pushing the boundaries of music forward in the widest possible variety of styles.

The way in which the music of our time interacts with the music of the past is an ever more fascinating subject as the century draws to its close, and threading its way through our programmes alongside the premieres is a strand of old music re-imagined and re-created by twentieth-century composers, from Stravinsky's *Pulcinella* and *The Fairy's Kiss* through to transcriptions by Ravel, Elgar, Schoenberg, Robin Holloway and others.

Taking over the direction of the Proms is surely the most enjoyably daunting challenge the musical world has to offer. From my three predecessors, William Glock, Robert Ponsonby and John Drummond, I have inherited a uniquely flourishing institution whose bold programmes, committed artists and responsive audiences are the envy of the world. They have set the highest standards and I hope we shall match them. I'm grateful to all the performers, especially the BBC's indispensable orchestras, singers and conductors, for rising to the challenges we have offered, and I am heavily in debt to the new Proms team, under its administrator (and my close collaborator) Stephen Maddock, who have launched this new-look Guide – don't miss the CD in the back cover! – and a host of new initiatives at double speed.

I hope that all our programmes will encourage you to take a few risks, to sample the unknown, and to participate in that uniquely welcoming and exciting atmosphere that only the Proms can offer. Enjoy the summer.

Nicholas Kenyon

Nicholas Kenyon *Controller, BBC Radio 3*

YOU MUST REMEMBER THIS...

MUSICIANS' BENEVOLENT FUND

Music's own Charity

DO SEND A DONATION TO-DAY TO
THE HONORARY TREASURER OF THE
MUSICIANS' BENEVOLENT FUND

Reproduced from
Elgar Memorial Concert
Programme 1934.

OUR WORK IS AS IMPORTANT TODAY AS IT WAS 75 YEARS AGO.

Please send a donation, large or small.

MUSICIANS
BENEVOLENT FUND

MBF 75 1921-96

ROOM G2, 16 OGLE STREET, LONDON W1P 8JB. REGISTERED CHARITY No. 228089

Tune in.
Turn on.
Listen.

Musical tastes may differ, but no one would deny the power of music to lift the soul. As a worldwide group dedicated to spreading pleasure and enjoyment to all age-groups through visual and audio entertainment, we are proud to be associated with this event.

 THORN EMI

THORN EMI plc
4 Tenterden Street
Hanover Square
London W1A 2AY
Telephone: 0171 355 4848

Making passionate love to history
BACH

PICTURES AT AN EXHIBITION

"All three versions have a right to exist"

Recreation Myths

Gerard McBurney explores composers who have 'made passionate love to history'

THERE IS AN odd tradition of being patronising towards music that is not purely 'itself', that borrows from other music, whether quoting from it, varying it, modelling itself upon it, parodying it, or just rearranging it. It is odd because most music depends on memories of other music, and innumerable are the compositions which would not exist at all but for specific other compositions which existed before them. But it is a strange inheritance of old ideas of 'originality' to dismiss work that depends on other work as impure and second-rate, as though the re-composer were trying to swindle us, or had just not done enough work.

Behind this puritanical attitude lurk hoary and persistent notions about the primacy of the author's intentions. There's a view, for example, that Musorgsky's own orchestration of his *Boris Godunov* must be better and truer than those later ones by Rimsky-Korsakov or Shostakovich simply because it alone represents the original composer's original intentions. And to betray these would be in some way to betray Musorgsky. The Russian conductor Gennady Rozhdestvensky once dismissed this proposition with the words: 'All three versions have a right to exist'.

In a similar vein, one could point out that Ravel's orchestration of *Pictures at an Exhibition* does not diminish Musorgsky's original conception for piano. It exists alongside it, as do all those other versions for orchestra, organ, brass band or whatever.

One of the simplest reasons why composers rewrite pieces, by themselves or by someone else, is the entirely practical one of making a performance possible. But even on these occasions, the real reasons can still turn out to be a bit more complicated than might at first appear. It may be, for example, that Elgar and Stokowski orchestrated Bach keyboard works because they felt that the orchestra-loving audiences of their own day didn't really know this music in its original form. On the other hand, even a few bars of one of their transcriptions (and they recomposed in very different styles) make it clear that what is really going on is not just a mechanical rewriting, but something like a sensuous dialogue between the arrangers' present and Bach's past – what Edmund White calls 'making passionate love to history'.

But time passes, and the expectations of audiences when they listen to Bach, or indeed when they listen to a symphony orchestra, change. So the music of

Bach, which seemed to Elgar and Stokowski to be a part of the past, now seems to us to be a rather different part of the past than it seemed to them. And the grand orchestral styles that seemed to them to be part of the present, are now already for us part of the past (though not the *same* part of the past as Bach!).

And so now, when we listen to Elgar's arrangement of the C minor Fantasia and Fugue, we are taking part in something that is different from what either Bach or Elgar intended: a three-way encounter between Bach's present, Elgar's recreation of the past in terms of his own present, and what is now our present and the way we listen to both these past composers in the summer of 1996.

There are those who disapprove of cross-temporal encounters of this kind, finding the tangled mixture of historical implications and perspectives ugly and unclear, but it would seem curmudgeonly to deny that they are interesting. If we now find it hard to see what Elgar's view of the C minor Fantasia and Fugue has to tell us about Bach (and that is our problem, not Elgar's), we should at the very least find that it still tells us something about the way Elgar himself listened.

Sometimes it is evident from the manner and detail of an arrangement that the re-composer is perfectly self-conscious about the deeper implications of what he or she is doing. When Schoenberg transformed Brahms's G minor Piano Quartet into something designed to sound rather like Brahms's Symphony No. 5, he too seems to have felt that such an orchestration would bring this music to a wider public. But at the same time, and far more importantly, he was deliberately setting out to achieve something that went beyond the passionate but generalised homages of Elgar and Stokowski into a detailed and highly personal examination of the way the older composer's music sounds, the way in which it is put together, and, most

profoundly, the way in which Brahms's musical language connected directly with his own. In making this transcription, Schoenberg was addressing his musical parentage, trying to understand where he himself came from.

Perhaps he was also trying to do something similar when he made the rarely-heard full-orchestral version of one of the greatest of his own early works, the Chamber Symphony No. 1. Maybe – and he would not have been the first composer to have done this – he was looking back affectionately, and even longingly, to the wonderful vitality and inspiration of his youth. But there again, he was probably also hoping that the piece would be performed a bit more often.

There are other reasons why composers return to their own earlier work. We are often told that Bach and Handel (among others) recycled music because it was expedient to do so, or so as not to 'waste a good idea'; but it may just as often have been because a particular compositional context demanded a particular solution, and this turned out to be one that the composer knew was already to be found in a previous work.

Below

Modest Musorgsky

Below

Maurice Ravel

Stravinsky, notoriously, revised a number of his older pieces when he got to America in order (and he himself could have fostered this story) to ensure the protection of his own copyright. But at the same time he also revised what he thought needed revising on the basis of his experience as a conductor and his changing compositional tastes. And he also reused music that would otherwise have gone to waste – notably in the Symphony in Three Movements, which is said to include considerable chunks he originally wrote for a projected film about St Bernadette. But it is as the self-conscious reuser of other people's material, their styles and ideas, that Stravinsky is most famous, and it is *Pulcinella* that most spectacularly embodies this aspect of his character. Stravinsky's own story of how he came to write this piece is at once a potent myth of the twentieth-century artist preying on the creations of an earlier age and a splendidly amusing personal anecdote. Apparently, Dyagilev presented him with eighteenth-century manuscripts of music he supposed to be by Pergolesi, and when the composer examined them he found that there were blank staves on which he himself could write additions, alterations and intrusions by no means in the style of the original.

Recent scholars have suggested that there might be a fair bit of exaggeration in this story, and that the amount that he actually wrote directly on to eighteenth-century manuscript paper might have been less than he suggested. But evidently Stravinsky the Russian story-teller wanted at the very least to shock people with the idea of ruthlessly mutilating ancient objects and to suggest something of the enthusiastic impertinence with which he approached the task of turning somebody else's music into a ballet of his own. The fact that the somebody else was not, on the whole, Pergolesi, only adds to the ironic stance of the venture.

The spirit of *Pulcinella* was not new in Stravinsky's work. Both *Petrushka* and *The Rite of Spring* depend on already existing materials (Russian street music and Lithuanian folk songs, respectively), and this vein was to continue throughout his life, in encounters with his beloved Tchaikovsky in *The Fairy's Kiss*, right on to the Wolf, Bach and Gesualdo transformations of his old age.

And the spirit of *Pulcinella* lives on beyond the life and work of Stravinsky. The particular, and sometimes peculiarly painful, self-conscious play with the borrowed rags of the musical past has remained an intense preoccupation. Indeed, rather than rejecting the music of the past, as a previous generation attempted to do, composers today seem to welcome it and make it their own. When Poul Ruders toys with a chorus from *Dido and Aeneas* in his *Concerto in Pieces*, or Robin Holloway conjures up a whole host of enchanted evenings with French angels by reinventing Chabrier, or Sir Peter Maxwell Davies uses a fragment of Medieval plainsong as the starting-point from which to address the great issues of more recent symphonic thought, each is in some way appealing to our sense of the sound of the past, to the way in which we remember other music.

We've made the world's most aerodynamic cars before.
But you weren't able to buy them.

Mercedes-Benz
Engineered like no other car.

Moving the

passions

David Wyn Jones assesses the immediate and lasting appeal of Joseph Haydn

Above
A ticket for one of Haydn's London concerts

Left
A performance of *The Creation* in Vienna in 1808

Right
Haydn with the score of the 'Drumroll' Symphony

'LIKE OUR OWN SHAKESPEARE, HE MOVES AND GOVERNS THE PASSIONS AT WILL.' These were the words that greeted Joseph Haydn in the *Morning Chronicle* on 12 March 1791, following his first public appearance in London. At the age of fifty-nine Haydn had just entered the most challenging period in his long creative life. After thirty years of faithful service as Kapellmeister to the Hungarian noble family the Esterházys, he had travelled to London to be resident composer at a subscription concert series organised by Johann Peter Salomon.

Haydn's music was not new to London: he had been the dominant composer in the city's rich musical life for the previous ten years, with practically all concerts including a work by him. It was virtually a Haydn fever – a new phenomenon in the history of music in which public popularity was not dependent on the physical presence of the composer. Although London was an extreme instance of this enthusiasm, Haydn's music was well known throughout Europe, from the Protestant north to the Catholic south, in genteel drawing rooms and aristocratic salons, as well as in public concert halls.

In London in 1791 Haydn was overwhelmed by this popularity, but he was saddened, too, by the fact that Mozart's music was comparatively unknown and certainly undervalued – 'a subject about which I have been sermonising them every day', as he wrote in a letter back to Vienna.

The *Morning Chronicle* paid Haydn the ultimate British compliment of comparison with Shakespeare. The journalist refers to 'moving the passions', an ability that the nineteenth and twentieth centuries were to deny Haydn's music as listeners recognised its skill but undervalued its commitment. Brahms was one of the few composers in the Romantic era to appreciate the passion as well as the craftsmanship of Haydn. He famously remarked of the slow movement of Symphony No. 88: 'I want my Tenth Symphony to be like this'.

Haydn's movement represents the composer at his most melodically generous, but he liked momentarily to discomfort too, providing that feeling of *frisson* that captivated listeners in the age of sensibility. The contrasts of the slow movement are, in turn, contained within a standard four-movement structure that displays other 'passions': enormous rhythmic energy in the first movement, what might be called rustic swagger in the minuet, and comic high spirits in the finale.

Such contrasts are characteristic of Haydn's symphonies composed in the 1780s and 1790s, and reflect a distinctive aspect of his musicianship. Unlike many of his contemporaries – most notably Mozart and Beethoven – he was not a virtuoso performer (he never played a concerto in a public concert), but he relished contact with an audience in much the same way that a virtuoso performer does.

The famous, unexpected loud chord in the slow movement of the 'Surprise' Symphony was a typical gimmick, designed, said Haydn, to 'frighten the ladies'. Later generations came to patronise the gimmicks – 'The Farewell', 'The Hen', 'The Clock' 'The Drumroll' and so on – without appreciating the context in which they occur.

The drumroll which opens Symphony No. 103 heralds a movement that makes inspired and wholly unexpected use of the music of the slow introduction. In eighteenth-

century London and elsewhere, there is ample testimony that Haydn's public recognised this sheer power of composition, the ability to reason and argue in music without becoming abstruse or difficult. Haydn's supreme mastery of the grammar and syntax of musical language is most keenly appreciated in his quartets and the best of the piano trios, the latter still unjustly neglected; they are a marvel of witty and learned discourse.

As a dutiful Kapellmeister at the Esterházy court from the 1760s to the 1780s Haydn would have been aware of his increasing international fame. His two visits to London in the 1790s enabled him to experience it at first hand, with palpable effects on his music. Indeed, as the composer became conscious of his universal appeal, there is a feeling that he willingly accepted the responsibility of

Above

The Esterházy Palace at Eisenstadt in the early nineteenth century

Left

Title-page of a piano arrangement of *The Creation*, published in 1800

being public property; from being Kapellmeister to an Austro-Hungarian court, Haydn had moved to being Kapellmeister to the whole of civilised Europe. At the same time, he never resigned as Esterházy Kapell-meister, holding the position through the two London visits and right up to his death in 1809. His music reflects this biographical paradox.

For instance, the immediate audiences for the *Mass in Time of War* of 1796 were congregations in Catholic churches in Vienna and Eisenstadt. But Haydn's Mass conveys broader concerns than liturgical services for the ordination of a priest or a nameday of an Esterházy princess, choosing to evoke the troubled atmosphere of the whole of Napoleonic Europe. While widespread distribution for the Mass in Catholic Europe was to be expected, Haydn's international fame meant that the firm of Breitkopf & Härtel in Protestant Leipzig was able to publish it – a rare honour for any item of church music.

An even more striking instance of a work that transcended religious and geographical boundaries was his oratorio *The Creation* (1798). Based on a text that Haydn had acquired in Protestant England, it was composed and first performed in Catholic Austria. It was initially stimulated by hearing the English oratorios of Handel, while its content reflects Haydn's unparalleled experience as a composer of symphonies, operas and masses.

The subject matter – the creation as told in the first book of Genesis – could not be more all-embracing. In the decades before the ravages of the Industrial Revolution began to be felt, many philosophers, writers and artists viewed the world as a perfect balance of differing interests, often making the parallel between the timeless working of nature and that of a watch. In *The Creation* Haydn carefully assembles the watch in our presence, lovingly describing the properties of each component before finally evoking the majesty of the whole.

This oratorio, one of the grandest products of the eighteenth century, makes full use of Haydn's creative responses: thoughtful and considered, charming and comic, overwhelming and inspiring. Here Haydn does, indeed, move and govern the passions at will.

Haydn's Creation, *with the BBC Symphony Orchestra and Chorus conducted by Andrew Davis, and soloists Juliane Banse, Hans Peter Blochwitz and Wolfgang Schöne, opens the 1996 Proms*

Above
Juliane Banse

Right
Hans Peter Blochwitz,
Wolfgang Schöne and
Andrew Davis

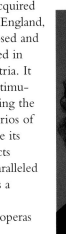

MUSICIANS

Play an instrumental part in the Royal Marines.

If you're male or female, sixteen to twenty-eight years of age, love music, and have an aptitude to play one or two instruments, then **ATTENTION.** The Royal Marines Band Service is currently looking for candidates to enrol for a select number of places at the Royal Marines School of Music. You'll receive over two years' training to a very high standard in a variety of instruments. As well as traditional military band music, you will earn as you learn to play jazz, pop, classical, light concert and big band music. You could find yourself taking part in the Edinburgh Festival, Beating Retreat on Horse Guards Parade or even a Cup Final at Wembley. So, if you're looking for your musical career to move up a scale or two, call us today on **0345 300 123** or return the coupon. Hurry, the closing date is soon. So MOVE IT, MOVE IT, MOVE IT.

▪▪

The Royal Marines are looking for men and women to fill vacancies now. Find out more at your local Jobcentre or send to: The Royal Navy and Royal Marines Careers Service, Dept (MA96819), FREEPOST 4335, Bristol BS1 3YX. No stamp needed. http://www.open.gov.uk/navy/rnhm.htm

NAME (Mr, Mrs, Miss) _____

ADDRESS _____

_____

POSTCODE _____ DATE OF BIRTH _____

TELEPHONE _____

We are equal opportunities employers under the Race Relations Act and welcome enquiries and applications from all ethnic groups.
Normally you should have been a UK resident for the past five years.

ROYAL MARINES
BAND SERVICE

See the world. Differently.

DON'T DREAM IT
DRIVE IT

RULE BRITANNIA

The XJ Sport really is a Great British car. With its high performance 3.2 and 4.0 litre engines, it's well-capable of raising the tempo. The ride and handling is precise, and the subtle blend of luxury and technology is perfectly orchestrated. And with prices from £31,829.00*, it's certainly music to the ears.

**For more information, or to arrange a test drive,
call Freephone (0800) 708060 or fax your details to 0171 611 6968**

*Manufacturers recommended retail price, correct at time of going to press, for an XJ Sport 3.2 Manual, including cost of delivery, number plates and a full tank of petrol.

Royal Philharmonic

Britain's and Classic FM's
national orchestra

50
144

Anniversary year
1946–1996

Royal Philharmonic Orchestra at the Royal Albert Hall

50TH ANNIVERSARY SEASON 1996/7

Conductors

DANIELE GATTI
THE LORD MENUHIN
YURI TEMIRKANOV
SIR CHARLES MACKERRAS
SIR PETER MAXWELL DAVIES
VERNON HANDLEY
VALERY GERGIEV
OWAIN ARWEL HUGHES

Programmes including

VERDI
Requiem

BERLIOZ
Symphonie Fantastique

SHOSTAKOVICH
Symphony No 10

WALTON
Belshazzar's Feast

Funded by
THE ARTS COUNCIL OF ENGLAND

CLASSIC *f*M

ROYAL ALBERT HALL

For a **FREE** brochure giving full
details of the concerts and dates,
please send this form to:

MARKETING DEPARTMENT,
ROYAL PHILHARMONIC ORCHESTRA,
FREEPOST (NO STAMP NECESSARY)
LONDON EC1B 1RP

Name ....

Address ....

....

Postcode .... Daytime tel ....

Barbican Visiting Orchestras Season

Autumn 1996

Anne Sofie von Otter

Richard Hickox

Sir Simon Rattle

Bournemouth Symphony Orchestra (20-22 Sep)
Richard Hickox
Elgar's three greatest choral works,
The Dream of Gerontius, *The Apostles* and *The Kingdom*

City of Birmingham Symphony Orchestra (4 Oct / 22 Nov)
Sir Simon Rattle
Haydn - *The Seasons*
Concert including music by Wagner

Royal Scottish National Orchestra (26 Sep)
Alexander Lazarev

BBC National Orchestra of Wales (30 Sep)
Mark Wigglesworth

Orpheus Chamber Orchestra (10 Oct)

Les Arts Florissants (14 Dec)
William Christie
Rameau's *Les Fetes d'Hébé*

Great Orchestras of the World

Moscow Philharmonic Orchestra (8 Oct)
Nikolai Demidenko

Danish Radio Symphony Orchestra (28 Oct)
Ulf Schirmer; Joshua Bell

Royal Concertgebouw Orchestra (3 Nov)
John Eliot Gardiner; Anne Sofie von Otter

San Francisco Symphony Orchestra (10 Nov)
Michael Tilson Thomas

Please send me details of the **Barbican Visiting Orchestras Season**

Name _____

Address _____

Daytime telephone number _____

Please send to: Barbican Centre Marketing Department, Freepost,
London 2089, London EC2B 2QB

Barbican Centre

Box Office 0171 638 8891 (9am - 8pm daily)

CORPORATION
OF LONDON

Owned, funded and
managed by the
Corporation of London

Prophet with honour

Mendelssohn's *Elijah* was premiered in Birmingham 150 years ago. Nicholas Temperley accounts for its enduring popularity in Britain

THE ILLUSTRATED LONDON NEWS PICTURE LIBRARY AKG LONDON HANYA CHLALA

Left The first performance of Mendelssohn's *Elijah* at Birmingham Town Hall as seen in the Illustrated London News (29 August 1846)

Top Left Richard Hickox

Top Right Bryn Terfel

Below Mendelssohn in 1846

SOON AFTER THE great success of *St Paul* at the Birmingham Festival in 1837, Mendelssohn set to work on a second oratorio. His choice fell on the story of Elijah, most vengeful of the Old Testament prophets. At that time he was brooding on the corruptions of modern life, especially in Berlin. His answer was to bring forth a work that would reassert the moral and musical power of the old values.

Yet it seems clear that *Elijah* was intended chiefly for an English audience. When the hoped-for commission came from the Birmingham Festival committee in June 1845, he set about his task in earnest. He worked with a German libretto, but he corresponded at length with his chosen English translator, offering to alter the notes to preserve the Authorised Version that meant so much to his English audiences. His continuing love affair with the English public (and royalty) must have been a powerful stimulus to his creative effort.

Mendelssohn conducted the first performance at Birmingham Town Hall on 26 August 1846. The reception was rapturous: as *The Times* said, 'Never was there a more complete triumph – never a more thorough and speedy recognition of a great work of art'. The music was inventive and powerful, but used familiar idioms and procedures, avoiding radical experiments *à la* Berlioz, which the Birmingham audience might have thought irreverent. As Wagner enviously admitted in 1855, Mendelssohn had understood, better than any leading composer, the devoutly religious feeling of the English, who treated an oratorio performance almost as an act of worship.

Another probable reason for the overwhelming success of *Elijah* was the religious climate that existed in England at the time. Newman's defection to Rome the previous year caused anxieties among the Protestant majority, as did the steady erosion of belief due to the growth of rationalism and the progress of science. A reassertion of the old faith, miracles and all, with punishment of idolaters, was deeply satisfying – especially to Nonconformists and Evangelical Anglicans.

Mendelssohn conducted a revised version in April 1847 at Exeter Hall, London, under the auspices of the Sacred Harmonic Society. After this double triumph, 'the' *Elijah* (as the Victorians called it) was immediately canonised in Britain, enjoying a status second only to 'the' *Messiah*. It has remained a favourite with the British public to this day.

Richard Hickox conducts and Bryn Terfel sings Elijah in Prom 48, 150 years to the day since the oratorio's premiere

Oxford

For excellence in the publishing of choral works and collections, scholarly editions, educational and tutorial music, and an internationally-performed contemporary list

music

Eleanor Alberga

Gerald Barry

Michael Berkeley

Benjamin Britten

John Buller

Martin Butler

Andrew Carter

Gordon Crosse

Michael Finnissy

Roberto Gerhard

Edward Harper

Alun Hoddinott

Constant Lambert

Libby Larsen

William Mathias

Elis Pehkonen

Gerald Plain

Anthony Powers

Alan Rawsthorne

John Rutter

Robert Sherlaw Johnson

Howard Skempton

Hilary Tann

Phyllis Tate

Ralph Vaughan Williams

William Walton

David Willcocks

Repertoire Promotion Department

Oxford University Press

3 Park Road

London NW1 6XN

Tel: 0171 724 7484

Fax: 0171 723 5033

Sales, Copyright, Hire, Editorial:

Music Department

Oxford University Press

Walton Street, Oxford

OX2 6DP

Tel: 01865 56767

Fax: 01865 267749

Your car can say a lot
about you. Or you
can speak for yourself.

The
master builder

Andrew Huth considers the music of Anton Bruckner in his centenary year

T HE DRAWBACK of being a late developer is that you will probably have to wait a long time for anyone to pay you much attention. Bruckner was already forty-two when he produced his First Symphony, over sixty before he gained much success in his own country, and had been dead for about seventy years before he was really accepted in Britain.

Our critics repeatedly claimed that his music 'wouldn't travel', or even that 'the English didn't want Bruckner'. The audience certainly didn't care for the Seventh Symphony when Henry Wood conducted it in 1903 – fifty-five years had to pass before another Bruckner Symphony, No. 4, was heard at the Proms. The centenary of his birth in 1924 passed quite unnoticed here, and it was only in the 1960s that we began to realise what we'd been missing.

Bruckner grew up in the Austrian countryside, the son and grandson of poor village schoolmasters, in a semi-feudal society hardly touched by the Enlightenment, let alone the ideas of the French Revolution or nineteenth-century Liberalism. His earliest instruction was from the Church, and his lifelong devotion to the Church's teaching was absolute. He began composing when he was a child,

Left Bruckner around 1890

Right The case of Bruckner's organ at St Florian, near Linz

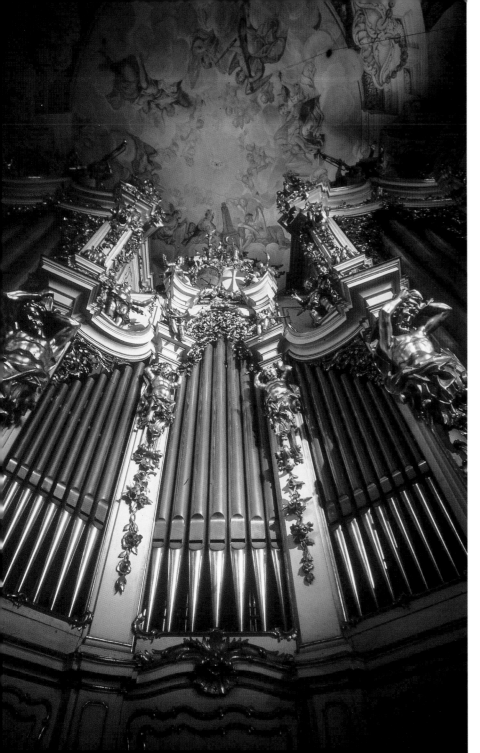

and reached middle age without giving much sign of originality. He seemed more interested in studying than in creating, eagerly gathering certificates and diplomas, acquiring a formidable technical armoury, but too shy to branch out on his own. It would have been the most natural thing for such a man to have become a worthy local composer, turning out undistinguished music for liturgical use.

But then, at around the age of forty, the dam finally burst. Bruckner wrote three great masses in quick succession, and then the highly original First Symphony, which he conducted in Linz, where he had been working for ten years as cathedral organist. Soon afterwards he moved to Vienna, where he was to live, not very happily, for the rest of his life, and where the remaining eight symphonies were composed.

He cut a poor figure in smart Viennese society. He had a thick local accent and wore dreadful clothes. His deep respect for authority led him to behave with appalling deference towards the luminaries of Music, Church and State. It didn't do him much good. Franz Liszt, sporting a cassock and dog-collar since 1865, squirmed with irritation when addressed as 'Your Grace, most reverend Herr Canonicus', and promptly lost the score of the Second Symphony which

Bruckner wished to dedicate to him. Other dedicatees of the symphonies included Richard Wagner, the King of Bavaria, the Emperor of Austria and God. Of these, the only one to offer Bruckner the slightest practical help was the Emperor, who subsidised the cost of printing the Eighth Symphony.

Although Bruckner's background was strictly traditional and orthodox, he was also devoted to the most radical music of the day. In 1862 he encountered that of Wagner, and its impact was overwhelming. Wagner's philosophical and dramatic ideas were of no importance to him. What captivated him was the orchestral sonority, the expressive chromatic harmony, and above all the control of a vastly extended time-scale, which he was to transfer from the music drama to the 'abstract' symphony.

Vienna was at that time a battleground where the partisans of Brahms and those of Wagner hurled abuse at one another, and it was Bruckner's misfortune to find himself right in the firing line. His naive pride in

Symfonie in Dmoll
Sr. Hochwohlgeboren
Herrn Herrn
Richard Wagner
dem unerreichbaren,
weltberühmten und
erhabenen Meister
der Dicht- und Tonkunst
in tiefster Ehrfurcht
gewidmet von
Anton Bruckner.

the friendship of The Master earned him a reputation as a 'Wagnerian Symphonist' that was enough to damn him in conservative circles.

Most artists have to put up with the hostility of enemies. Few have suffered so much from their friends. Many of these took a patronising attitude, and unwittingly did enormous damage by suggesting 'improvements' which they believed were necessary to make Bruckner's music acceptable. The disciples who rescored and rewrote his music were admirers of the details, but often failed to grasp the whole; they thrilled to the glorious moments of the climaxes, but could not perceive the structure that justified them.

Although Bruckner was persuaded to sanction the publication of 'revised' editions, he took the precaution of carefully preserving his original manuscripts 'for a later time'. The original versions of his scores were not published until the 1930s. But just when the 'Bruckner problem' should have been finally cleared up, there came admiration of an even less welcome kind: the clouds of incense with which pious devotees shrouded his music ('God's minstrel', 'Liturgical symphonies', 'Masses without words', they mumbled earnestly) had to compete with the altogether nastier fog of nationalist propaganda. Bruckner was now expected to fulfil the role of star Aryan composer.

Bruckner's contemporaries – supporters and enemies alike – naturally judged him by the standards of their own time, whereas it now seems quite striking how far apart from the concerns of the late nineteenth century he actually was. He created a synthesis

Above Jane Glover conducts Bruckner motets in Prom 71

Centre The dedication of the Third Symphony to Richard Wagner

Left Günter Wand conducts the Sixth Symphony in Prom 61

CLIVE BARDA AKG LONDON BMG/RCA RED SEAL

"*The slow, deliberate pacing demands intense concentration from the players, and an active engagement on the part of the listener*"

between Classical traditions, the vast knowledge of counterpoint he had acquired during his years of study, and the sonority and broad dimensions he found in Wagner. The spirit of his music, however, is free of much that characterised his age, and is actually as far from the spirit of Wagner as any music could be. It is free of heavy Romantic pathos, it is not redolent of sensuality or eroticism. Bruckner completely avoided many of the negative features of his time: he offers grandeur without bombast, tenderness without sentimentality, contemplation without false religiosity. Instead of exalting the individual ego, this music unfolds with a grand objectivity of expression.

This was not easily achieved. Bruckner's modest personality obviously concealed something very tough indeed; but he was prey all his life to severe nervous problems, to which his personal loneliness and insecurity made him very vulnerable. Beneath his craving for order and his firmly-held religious faith there probably lurked something far more chaotic and unstable than the music generally allows one to suspect. On the rare occasions when hints of black disorder come into the open (as in parts of the Eighth and Ninth Symphonies) the effect can be deeply disturbing – but the enduring impression in Bruckner is always of splendour and magnificence, whatever demons he had to overcome in the course of his quest.

Grandeur can't be hurried, and it can't be expressed in epigrams. Bruckner needs time to construct his musical worlds, and a good performance of a Bruckner symphony is one in which every detail takes its place in the scheme, and where there is a compelling sense of revelation as the music gradually unfolds. The slow, deliberate pacing demands intense concentration from the players, and an active engagement on the part of the listener, but the rewards are great indeed.

All great music is unique – that is part of its greatness, and often the reason why it is at first difficult to understand. After the passage of a hundred years, however, Bruckner's symphonies have come to hold a very special and honourable position in our musical life. His hard-won personal vision has now become something that we can all share, opening our minds onto broad musical landscapes whose horizons stretch far into the distances of time and space.

Below right Simon Rattle conducts Symphony No. 7 in Prom 57

Below Gennady Rozhdestvensky conducts the Second Symphony in Prom 15

WHSmith and EMI present

The Classics Collection

An excellent introduction to the very best classical music.

Over 40 titles on CD and cassette available from WHSmith music stockists.

CD's £7.99 · Cassettes £4.99 each

There's more to classical music at

WHSmith

cut here

£2 off *any CD or* £1 off *any cassette*

from the EMI classic collection with this voucher

Terms and Conditions

1 This voucher entitles the bearer to save £2 off any CD or £1 off any cassette from the EMI Classics Collection. 2 Voucher valid until 31st October 1996.
3 Voucher may not be redeemed for cash or against any other purchase. 4 Offer is exclusive to WHSmith. 5 Only one voucher may be redeemed per purchase.
6 This voucher may not be combined with any other offer.

Staff Number

Till Number

Receipt Number

WHSmith Limited, Registered Office: Strand House, 7 Holbein Place, London. SW1W 8NR

One of life's more rewarding decisions.

KEF Reference Series

If only all decisions in life were as straightforward as this. The fact is that if you want the purest sound and the most uncompromising specification, it simply has to be New KEF Reference.

Every speaker must match our engineers' 'reference' prototype to an almost unbelievable tolerance of 0.5 decibels. This means you can be sure that the sound originally achieved at KEF will be recreated in your home. Exactly.

Our breakthrough Uni-Q® technology delivers an astonishing stereo image, its unique point source design, with the tweeter at the exact acoustic centre of the mid-range cone, lets you visualise the precise location of every performer on the stage. What's more, because of Uni-Q's smooth,

even dispersion you'll hear that incredible realism throughout the room. From speakers this good you'd expect outstanding bass performance. With KEF's famous 'coupled cavity' bass system, now further improved with interports, you get it. We go to similar extremes in perfecting every detail. Some you can't see, like Oxygen-Free Copper internal wiring or magnetic shielding (vital in Home Theatre). Some you can - sumptuously veneered cabinets with heavily gold-plated feet and terminals, for example.

In other words, each pair of Reference speakers is as close to perfection as KEF can make it.

When you know you can choose the best, would you willingly settle for anything less?

KEF®

The experience of sound

Aimez-vous Stravinsky?

Twenty-five years after the composer's death, Stephen Walsh asks whether we really understand his music

I T IS A STANDARD MYTH, much cultivated in the past by composers and their publicists, that great music is neglected or misunderstood in its own time. For one thing, who are we to suppose that we 'understand', say, Beethoven any better than the man who shouted 'L'Empereur!' at the first Parisian performance of the Fifth Symphony, just because we saturate ourselves in his music while ironing, or doing our homework, or (for heaven's sake!) chattering? For another thing, it's a demonstrable fact that nearly all the composers we admire now were also admired in their lifetimes, often just as exorbitantly.

Stravinsky is a good example. From that June evening in 1910 when *The Firebird* brought the house down at the Paris Opéra, its composer became one of the most famous, most publicised, most interviewed, most photographed, most talked-about artists of his day, one whose arrivals and departures were reported in the local press, whose views were sought on matters of public interest – the Russian question, the merits of air travel, the English climate – and whose endorsement of consumer products itself became a marketable commodity.

Left
Stravinsky, 1915, by
Jacques-Emile
Blanche

**Above, from left to
right** Stravinsky in
1929; Rehearsing The
Fairy's Kiss, 1947; At
BBC Maida Vale
Studios, 1961

His music was played, too, though it's fair to say that preference was nearly always given to a handful of spectacular early works and one or two later ones, like *Pulcinella* (with its arrangements of Pergolesi and others) and *The Fairy's Kiss*, which was Tchaikovsky with a modern *frisson*.

In the 1920s and after, Stravinsky promoted his own music by playing or conducting it. But it's obvious from his correspondence with promoters and agents, and from press reports in general, that the newer works he always tried to programme were of much less interest than the mere presence of their composer, this quasi-legendary figure whose *Rite of Spring* (itself rarely programmed, because of the number of rehearsals it needed) was reputed to be the most terrifying concatenation of sounds ever to assault the human ear. Would he have horns, or a forked tail?

'The American public has thought of him as a weird figure', one Chicago critic wrote during Stravinsky's first US tour in 1925, 'reared from the cradle on a diet of discord, preaching an evangel of ugliness, racking our nerves to create a sensation.' But in fact 'he has had an entirely logical evolution'. By the 1920s Stravinsky was no longer in the informed view the raving, child-snatching ogre of popular folklore ('eat your greens, or Stravinsky will get you'), but had become a cool, heartless intellectual, the inventor of a rectilinear music of steel and concrete: not an inspired maniac but a clanking machine. We may feel that these two viewpoints were equally wide of the mark. But, as Stravinsky's frequent and highly paid concert appearances performing his own music prove, they didn't add up to neglect.

Were they such 'misunderstandings' anyway? Take out the note of disapproval in each case, and you could argue that, on the contrary, they were perfectly fair assessments. As far as the 'machine' aspect is concerned, Stravinsky himself went out of his way to promote his 1920s music – works like the Concerto for Piano and Wind and the *Capriccio* – as cool and objective, anti-Romantic, very much a part of the 'Return to Order' preached by non-musician friends of his like Paul Valéry, Jean Cocteau and the religious philosopher Jacques Maritain. He *wanted* to be thought of as a composer whose heart was a working machine, not the irrational seat of the emotions, because he thought that 'expression' (a word he detested) was best achieved through 'form', whatever that might be.

He had even started thinking that way long before neo-Classicism as such was even a smoke-signal on the horizon. In an article he wrote about *The Rite of Spring* just before its chaotic first performance in 1913, he claimed to have excluded the stringed instruments from the work's prelude because they were 'too evocative, too much like the human voice', and brought forward the wind instruments as being 'drier, cleaner, less charged with facile expressiveness, and for that reason all the more moving, to my mind'.

But surely this is just an early sign of his over-developed taste for the unexpected. After all, *The Rite* was supposed to have originated in a dream – that most irrational of human functions – and it was undoubtedly written in a state of excitement, if not frenzy. Its composer was no machine at that time, but more a sort of medium. 'I am the vessel through which

The Rite passed', he said. But that was fifty years, and several changes of mind, later. In 1913, he was already realising the dangers of being typecast as a musical table-tapper, even before a note of the music had been heard in public.

Stravinsky himself was certainly wary of his reputation, and perhaps even allowed it to influence his creative direction, which may seem a very odd thing for a great artist to do. When he wrote his little bourgeois opera *Mavra* in 1922, he deliberately pulled the noses of his smart Paris admirers by dedicating it partly to Tchaikovsky, a composer they despised, partly to Glinka, a composer they hadn't heard of, and partly to Pushkin, a poet they couldn't read. *Apollo*, surely the most exquisitely refined and sweet-tempered of all twentieth-century masterpieces, must have been at least half-consciously aimed at those who had long since filed him away under 'Primitive, Dissonant, Unsuitable for mixed company'.

Stravinsky found it stimulating to wrong-foot his audience. He certainly did it often enough, especially, as a final coup in the 1950s, by starting to write brilliant serial works like *Agon* and *The Flood* and openly to admire Schoenberg

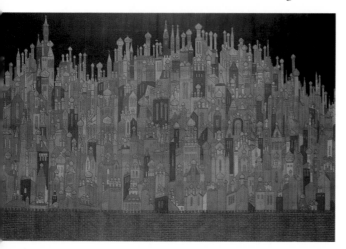

Below left
Backcloth by Natalia Goncharova for the revival of *The Firebird*

Below
Andrew Parrott conducts the Cantata, the Mass, and the Concerto for Piano and Wind in Prom 30

**Stravinsky Day
(11 August)
conductors:**

Left Daniel Harding
conducts *The Soldier's
Tale*

Below Oliver
Knussen conducts *The
Flood* and *The Fairy's
Kiss*

Below Dyagilev
(seated) with (left to
right) Stravinsky,
Cocteau and Satie.
Signed M. L., 1917

and Webern (not to mention Boulez and Stockhausen), leaving his fans embarrassed and confused at their well-documented distaste and contempt for all such music. Nadia Boulanger, the greatest fan of them all but a neo-Classicist to her bones, would glare at you through her spectacles and say, 'Stravinsky is the *only* composer who knows how to write serial music'.

The question we might ask ourselves today is whether we know and understand our Stravinsky any better, or even as well. What do we know of those late works – outwardly so forbidding and still so little played, yet written with exactly the same intention to invigorate and entertain as *Petrushka* and *The Rite of Spring*? What jet-set conductor would routinely programme *Oedipus Rex* or the Symphony in C, as he might Brahms's *German Requiem* or Beethoven's Fifth? The very fact that we still regard these works as 'modern music' (and perform them – or not – accordingly) is significant. Stravinsky not only died twenty-five years ago, but he was born a hundred and fourteen years ago, yet his work is still, to us, contemporary.

But then Bach and Beethoven are eternally contemporary as well, and if it comes to that our knowledge and understanding of their music is questionable too. We just feel more at home with them than with the composer of *The Soldier's Tale* and the *Symphonies of Wind Instruments*. Is that a sign that we understand them any better, or just that we've stopped listening to them? If much of Stravinsky still poses problems, still scares us a bit, perhaps that's no bad thing.

Sunday 11 August is Stravinsky Day at the Proms

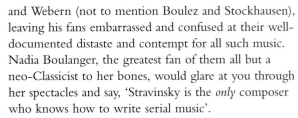

Left Programme for
the Ballets Russes
1923 season, showing
a set design by Picasso

Below Costume
design by Kenneth
Rowell for the Winds
in *The Fairy's Kiss* at
Covent Garden, 1960

> "...a feast of music–making that would be hard to equal anywhere in the world."
>

The Edinburgh International Festival. Fifty years of rave reviews.

There's nothing new about rave at the Edinburgh International Festival. It is what serious music lovers have been doing here for the last fifty years. For half a century now the world's greatest musicians have appeared on our stages. This year, our half centenary, promises to be one of the best ever. The programme includes two Gluck operas directed by two leading dance makers - Orfeo ed Euridice, directed by Mark Morris and Iphigenie auf Tauris, directed by Pina Bausch; the world premiere of James MacMillan's first full length opera, Ines de Castro and Houston Grand Opera's acclaimed production of Virgil Thomson's Four Saints in Three Acts, directed by Robert Wilson.

Add to the list names like Claudio Abbado, Christoph von Dohnányi, Kurt Masur, Andras Schiff, Evgeny Kissin and Bryn Terfel, to name but a few, and you will see why we're confident that audiences and critics will be raving once again. The fiftieth Edinburgh International Festival runs from 11-31 August 1996. For full programme call 0131 226 4001, for booking call 0131 225 5756 or write to Edinburgh International Festival, 21 Market Street, Edinburgh EH1 1BW.

fifty 50 FESTIVAL YEARS EDINBURGH 1996

Edinburgh
International FESTIVAL

11-31 August 1996.

Registered charity No.SCOO4694.

D·R·O·O·P·Y & B·R·O·W·N·S· BY ANGELA HOLMES

Photograph: Anthony Crickmay   Harpsichord by Andrew Wooderson – 01322 558326

DAYWEAR

CONCERT DRESSES

WEDDING GOWNS

MILLINERY

99 ST MARTINS LANE
LONDON WC2
0171 379 4514

16-17 ST CHRISTOPHERS PLACE
LONDON W1
0171 486 6458

1-2 PULTENEY BRIDGE
BATH
01225 463796

37-39 FREDERICK STREET
EDINBURGH
0131 225 1019

21 STONEGATE
YORK
01904 621458

16-18 QUEEN VICTORIA STREET
LEEDS
0113 234 1143

FOR YOUR ON STAGE
&
OFF STAGE WARDROBE

Left Pablo Picasso
Violin and Guitar, 1913

From the sunny Spanish shore

Tess Knighton surveys the Spanish strand in this year's Proms

Above Roberto Gerhard and Felipe Pedrell (seated), 1921

Right Gerhard, c1960

SPAIN: THE LAND OF SUNSHINE and sangria to holidaymakers, but in reality a country of contrasts reflected in the landscape and culture of each region. Linguistic and political differences are today acknowledged in the varying degrees of autonomy granted to Catalonia, Aragon, the Basque Country, Galicia and Andalusia. We are witnessing the disintegration of that sense of national identity, that 'Spanishness' fomented by the unification of Castile and Aragon through the marriage of Ferdinand and Isabella in the late fifteenth century and deliberately fostered – even enforced – by succeeding rulers.

What this will mean for the future of 'Spanish' music is not clear, but at the end of the nineteenth century the emphasis was firmly on a national identity in the arts. A national musical idiom was the dream of the Catalan composer and musicologist Felipe Pedrell (1841–1922), and his influence was decisive in the development of the greatest Spanish composer of the early twentieth century: Manuel de Falla.

1996 sees the fiftieth anniversary of Falla's death, as well as the centenary of the birth of another of Pedrell's protégés, Roberto Gerhard. A strong 'Spanish' theme runs through this year's Proms, with a number of rarely-heard works by Falla, Gerhard and their contemporaries, and the first London visit of the Joven Orquesta Nacional de España, roughly equivalent to our own National Youth Orchestra.

The orchestra was formed in 1983 by the Spanish Ministry of Culture, and serves the whole of the peninsula through quarterly gatherings in different regions. It has made three recordings of music by Falla, but for its UK debut has chosen to perform Gerhard's little-known cantata *The Plague*, a work commissioned by the BBC in the 1960s, together with two of the most popular Spanish (or Spanish-inspired) pieces: Rodrigo's *Concierto de Aranjuez* and Ravel's *Bolero*. The programme will be conducted by Edmon Colomer, until recently the orchestra's Principal Conductor, who has been largely responsible for the high standards and international recognition it has achieved in recent years.

The Plague, based on Albert Camus's novel,

Top left Falla (1932)
by Ignacio Zuluoga

Bottom left
Federico Francisco
Goya *The Healthy and
the Sick*

Below and right
Atlántida, La Scala,
Milan, 18 June 1962

Right Poster for the
premiere of *Atlántida*,
La Scala, 1962

Below Edmon
Colomer and the
Joven Orquesta
Nacional de España

represents Gerhard's mature style, in which any sense of 'Spanishness' has been subsumed into a highly original and personal musical idiom that is essentially European. Already in the *Seven Haiku*, written in 1922, well before Gerhard was forced to leave Spain after the defeat of the Republicans in the Civil War, the composer can be seen at a crossroads: the distinctive colours, melodic contours and rhythmic elements associated with Spanish music are integrated into a new context in which the influence of Schoenberg (with whom Gerhard studied at that time) is paramount. Yet Gerhard never forgot his earlier mentor Pedrell, and Promenaders will also have the chance to hear his delightful arrangements of some of the folk songs collected by Pedrell at the end of the nineteenth century.

Born in Catalonia on 25 September 1896, of Franco-Swiss descent, a pupil of Schoenberg in Berlin and a resident of Britain for the second half of his life, Gerhard was truly European. Falla, too, travelled abroad, and there is little doubt that his extended sojourn in Paris (1907–14) was crucial both to his development as a composer and in establishing his international profile.

Born a generation earlier than Gerhard, his aims were nurtured in a different climate. If Pedrell preached musical nationalism, it was Falla who had the technical resources and vision to realise the dream of a Spanish musical idiom. He was not alone: Albéniz and Granados were also protagonists of the Pedrell-inspired Spanish school, and composers outside Spain from Ravel to Rimsky-Korsakov drank deeply at the well of Spanish musical inspiration. Yet it was Falla, more than any other, who distilled the essence of Spain's varied musical traditions.

His source of inspiration was essentially the folk music of Andalusia. He was born in Cadiz and lived for many years in Granada, and it was the highly distinctive and inherently dramatic idiom of the *cante jondo* of the Andalusian gypsies that formed the initial impetus for his creation of a Spanish musical idiom. The foot-stamping, fiery rhythms and wailing, heart-piercing melodies of his earlier works – *La vida breve*, *El amor brujo* or *The Three-Cornered Hat* (which can also be heard during the season in its original version, *El corregidor y la molinera*) – draw most overtly on this tradition.

Another early piece, *Nights in the Gardens of Spain*, shares in the Andalusian flavour in its atmospheric depiction of the Moorish gardens of southern Spain, albeit in a less direct, more Impressionistic manner.

In his later works, Falla's distillation of the essence of native musical traditions became more abstract, less focused on melodic and rhythmic patterns and broader in musical reference. Perhaps the jewel in the crown of this year's Spanish theme is the first London performance of a suite from his last work, the scenic cantata *Atlántida*, given by the BBC Symphony Orchestra under the direction of the most distinguished of Spanish conductors, Rafael Frühbeck de Burgos, and featuring María Bayo, the young Spanish soprano who is surely set to follow in the footsteps of Victoria de los Angeles.

Falla, who had begun this, his most ambitious enterprise, as early as 1927, never finished it, though he continued to work on it in the last years of his life, despite increasingly poor health. By this time, he, like Gerhard, had left Spain, settling in Argentina. 'Who would have thought', he commented, delighting in the gentle irony, 'that I would finish in America the music of its discovery?' For *Atlántida*, based on a poem by the Catalan poet Jacinto Verdaguer, retells the myth of Hercules's conquests in the gardens of the Hesperides and the engulfing of Atlantis for the benefit of the young Columbus. As a grown man, Columbus never forgets the impact of this story, and finds confirmation in the dreams of Queen Isabella of his destiny to discover the New World.

It is an extraordinary, visionary work that called for Falla's broadest musical palette, from sixteenth-century Spanish polyphony to Stravinsky via the infusion of traditional elements, and representing that strange mix of sensuality and austerity that characterised both the man and his music.

Royal Philharmonic
Britain's and Classic FM's
national orchestra

50
Anniversary year
1946–1996

Golden Jubilee of the Royal Philharmonic Orchestra
in association with *The Malcolm Sargent Cancer Fund for Children*

ROYAL ALBERT HALL
SUNDAY 15 SEPTEMBER 1996
7.30PM

Ticket prices:
Stalls £27
2nd tier boxes £21
Front Arena £21
Rear Arena £16
Front Balcony (new seating) £16
Rear Balcony (new seating) £10
Restricted View Balcony £5

Conductors
THE LORD MENUHIN
YURI TEMIRKANOV
VALERY GERGIEV
SIR CHARLES MACKERRAS
SIR PETER MAXWELL DAVIES

Soloists
IDA HAENDEL *(violin)*
JAMES GALWAY *(flute)*
MARISA ROBLES *(harp)*
GEORGE McILWHAM *(bagpipes)*
BRYN TERFEL *(bass baritone)*

Programme to include
HANDEL   *Zadok the Priest*
          The Trumpet Shall Sound,
          The King Shall Rejoice
MOZART   *Flute and Harp Concerto*
MAXWELL
DAVIES   *Orkney Wedding*
DELIUS   *Walk to the Paradise Garden*
RAVEL   *Tzigane*
BORODIN   *Polovtsian Dances*

ROYAL CHORAL SOCIETY
BRIGHTON FESTIVAL CHORUS
MALCOLM SARGENT FESTIVAL CHOIR

ROYAL ALBERT HALL

Booking now open. Call the Royal Albert Hall on **0171 589 8212**

A World of Music

Founded on the great European traditions of instrument making and music publishing, the Boosey & Hawkes Group is today one of the world's foremost music companies.

Our international roster of twentieth-century composers is unrivalled and our instruments are played by performers throughout the world. In both advanced and developing countries we are exercising an important influence, as more people turn to music as a popular leisure pursuit.

In the field of music education, we are firmly committed to developing future generations of musicians by providing them with access to instruments and printed music of the highest quality.

From school concerts to the Proms, from bandrooms to opera houses, on radio and television, Boosey & Hawkes helps the world to enjoy the priceless gift of music.

Photography credits: Gerhard Estate (Gerhard), Hanya Chlala (Maxwell Davies), Deborah Feingold (Adams), Jack Shear (Rorem), Malcolm Crowthers (Schnittke).

Roberto Gerhard

BESSON LONDON

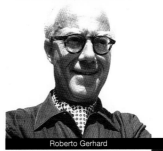
Igor Stravinsky

Sir Peter Maxwell Davies

Höfner

R Paesold

Dmitri Shostakovich

BUFFET Crampon & Cie A PARIS

John Adams

JULIUS KEILWERTH Saxophone

W. Schreiber

Ned Rorem

Serge Prokofieff

Alfred Schnittke

Jakob WINTER

Rescuing Leonore

David Cairns introduces the first version of Beethoven's operatic masterpiece

EVEN IF IT CANNOT be regarded as an alternative to *Fidelio,* the original version of Beethoven's opera is a work of great fascination and extraordinary power. *Leonore* – the title by which this version is now generally known, and which Beethoven himself wanted for the work – shows the composer struggling with the (to him unfamiliar) medium of opera, but rising to the challenge like the instinctive dramatic genius he was.

His inexperience betrayed him into excessive repetition within the musical numbers, and also led him to give too much prominence to the homely environment from which the mighty events of the opera gradually take shape. But the mixture of domestic comedy and heroic melodrama remained a central principle in the detailed revision which Beethoven undertook nine years later, in 1814, when the work as we know it took its final form.

The principle derived from Cherubini. In 1802 a season of 'rescue operas' by the French Revolutionary school of composers – prominent among them Cherubini's *Les deux journées* and *Lodoïska* – took Vienna by storm. Beethoven shared in the general enthusiasm. Not only was his orchestral style influenced by Cherubini's, but by early 1804 he had begun setting a German translation of a French libretto very much in the same mould: the story of a devoted, intrepid woman who seeks out her husband – a political prisoner held secretly in solitary

Above
A performance at the Theater an der Wien, in 1805 or 1806, around the time of the opera's premiere

Left
Ludwig van Beethoven

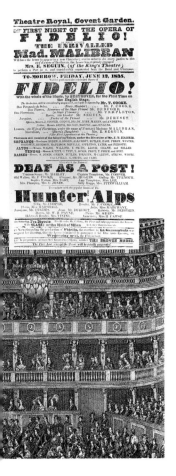

AKG LONDON ROYAL OPERA HOUSE ARCHIVES MARCO BORGGREVE

Left
Poster announcing performance of *Fidelio* at the Theatre Royal, Covent Garden, 1835

> "*Leonore* also includes beautiful music that Beethoven would later ruthlessly cut"

confinement – and saves him.

It may have been the very intensity of Beethoven's response, and not just his lack of experience of the theatre, that caused him problems. At a time in his life when his growing deafness and his longing for the ideal wife made him both identify with the suffering Florestan and project the heroic Leonore in the most exalted terms, the drama simply moved him too deeply.

But what marvellous sparks it struck from him, from the first! *Leonore* may not have the visionary final section of Florestan's scena, or the prisoners' farewell to the sunlight as they return to their cells, or 'Abscheulicher!', the great recitative that introduces

Leonore's aria, 'Komm, Hoffnung' – all of them added in the 1814 revision – but it has some of the opera's supreme inventions, among them the Canon Quartet (one bar longer than in *Fidelio*), 'Komm, Hoffnung', the first Prisoners' Chorus, the main section of Florestan's scena, the Dungeon Quartet and the duet 'O namenlose Freude'. Much in them would be modified in *Fidelio* (including one or two startlingly unconventional strokes); but their essence is there.

Leonore also includes beautiful music that Beethoven, for reasons of dramatic cogency or musical tautness, would later ruthlessly cut. As a whole, it enables us, with hindsight, to see him at work, striving to fashion a sprawling, richly abundant score into a masterpiece. It catches his primal response, imperfect but impassioned, magnificently on the wing, and, as such, demands to be heard.

John Eliot Gardiner conducts a rare performance of Leonore *with the Orchestre Révolutionnaire et Romantique in* Prom 36

Top right
John Eliot Gardiner

Right
Charlotte Margiono

Last tho

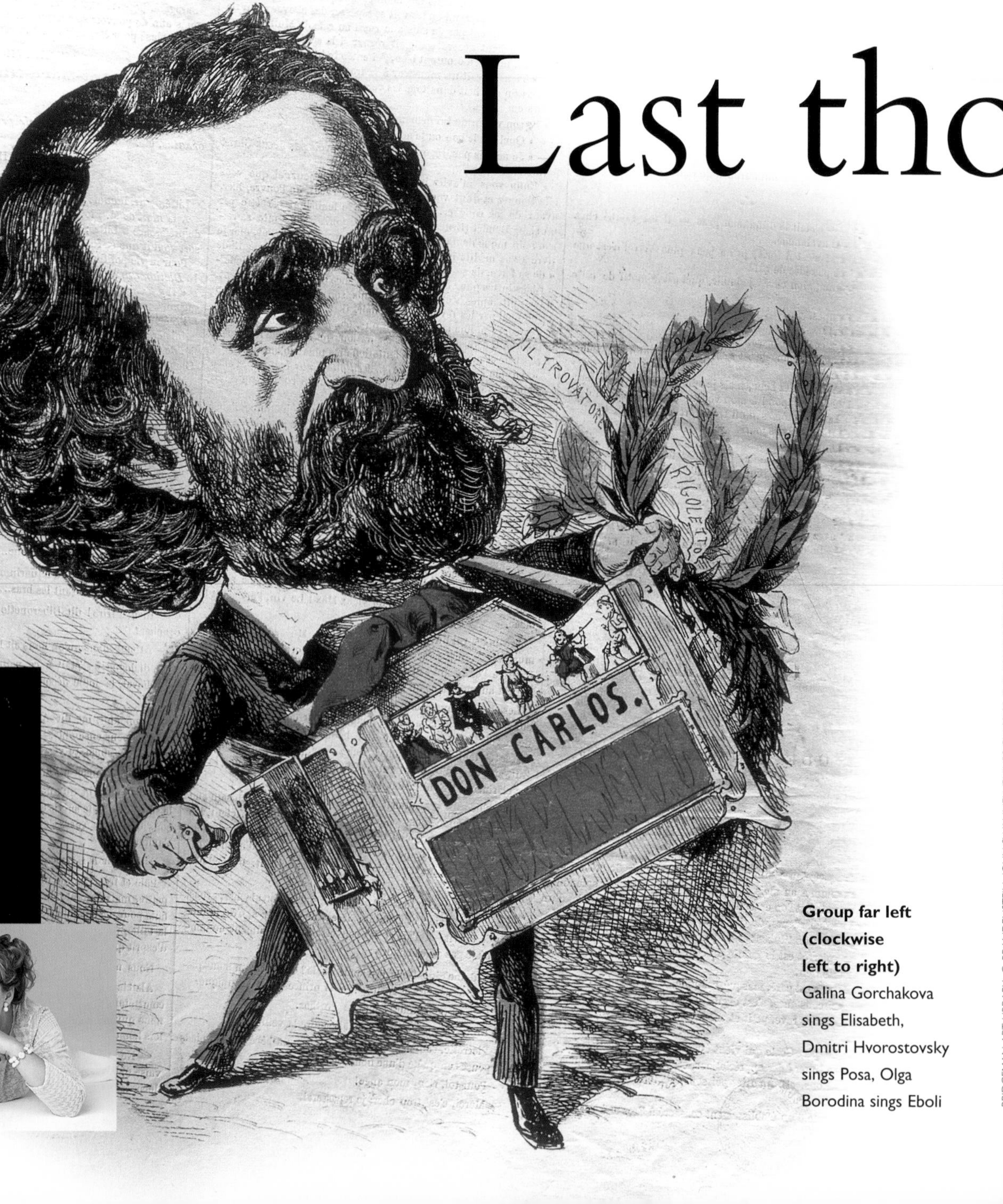

IL TROVATORE

RIGOLETTO

DON CARLOS.

**Group far left
(clockwise
left to right)**
Galina Gorchakova
sings Elisabeth,
Dmitri Hvorostovsky
sings Posa, Olga
Borodina sings Eboli

ughts on 'Carlos'

Andrew Porter introduces the final version of what is perhaps Verdi's greatest opera

Top Bernard Haitink

Above
Scene from the Royal
Opera production of
Don Carlos in 1985

Main picture
Caricature of Verdi

Far right
Verdi (with umbrella)

Don Carlos is Verdi's noblest, most ambitious opera. Five vivid characters, emotionally entangled, are caught in a web of State and Church where their decisions and actions affect not only their own lives but the destiny of all the subjects in Philip II's far-flung dominions.

Meyerbeer, long the leading *grand opéra* composer, died in 1864; Verdi welcomed an invitation to compose the Opéra's big new work for 1867, the year of Napoleon III's Universal Exhibition. He could use the Opéra resources – a stable company, chorus, and orchestra; lavish scenic provision, long months of rehearsal – with Meyerbeerian splendour, but more earnestly. Not 'effects without causes' – Wagner's phrase for Meyerbeer – but effects with meaning.

Verdi shaped the dramatic content himself. When the scenario was submitted to him, he asked for spectacle to be added (the *auto-da-fé*, with its processions and multiple choruses, was the result), but asked too for the addition of two duets from the original Schiller play: between Philip and Posa, and between Philip and the Grand Inquisitor.

He composed on the largest scale. Too large! In rehearsals the opera overran, many cuts were made before the first night, and more during the run. Even then, it remained an unwieldy work. At Covent Garden, three months after the Paris premiere, Act 1

(in Fontainebleau), the ballet, much of Elisabeth's last aria, and the final chorus were omitted. In 1882, with a Vienna production in prospect, the composer himself set about a revision: 'If there must be amputation, I'd rather wield the knife myself'. He, too, excised Act 1, the ballet, and the final chorus, but at the same time he reinstated dramatic points that had been obscured by the pre-premiere cuts, and recomposed many passages in a tauter manner.

He described the result as 'more practicable and also, I think, artistically better – more concise, more muscular'. He worked in French; but the revised opera had its premiere in Italian translation, at La Scala in 1884. Two years later, there appeared an edition in which the original Act 1 was joined to the four acts of the revision. And this is the version we hear at the Proms.

Complicated history! I tangled it further when in the Paris Opéra Library, in 1969, I found the forgotten, unpublished music that had been cut before the premiere; and the BBC brought it to life. So there's more fine *Don Carlos* music than any single performance can coherently compass. But the 1886 edition is the late, ample version ('permitted and approved by the illustrious composer') of his great, perhaps his greatest, opera.

Bernard Haitink directs the Royal Opera in the 1886 version of Don Carlos *in Prom 2. The French version is in the Royal Opera's Verdi Festival at Covent Garden*

A Winter's Fairy Tale

David Drew introduces a revival of a rarity by Kurt Weill

KATIE VANDYCK. BLACKSTONE STUDIOS, LONDON, COURTESY OF THE

T he Silver Lake (Der Silbersee) calls itself 'A Winter's Fairy Tale' but it concerns the harsh realities of a socially and economically divided world at a time of widespread unemployment. It was the last of Weill's three collaborations with the eminent playwright Georg Kaiser, and the very last score he completed before fleeing Hitler's Germany in March 1933.

Produced with notable success in Leipzig and in two other German cities during the brief period between Hitler's appointment as Chancellor in January 1933 and the Nazi seizure of power five weeks later, The Silver Lake was not seen again in Germany until many years after Hitler's defeat. It waited forty years for its first hearing abroad, but today is internationally recognised as one of Weill's finest scores, and the direct forebear of his and Brecht's song-and-dance cantata The Seven Deadly Sins.

On the face of it, The Silver Lake belongs to the same 'play-with-music' genre as The Threepenny Opera – a three-hour evening, of which about one hour is musical. As in The Threepenny Opera there are overtures and finales, strophic songs and some celebrated hits (including another 'Morität' in the shape of an overtly

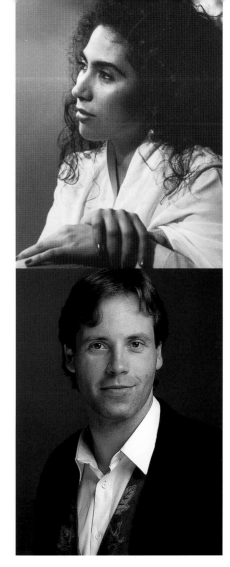

Top left
Kurt Weill (c1934)

Centre
Act 1, Scene 2 from
Der Silbersee, 1933

anti-fascist 'Ballad of Caesar's Death'). On closer inspection, however, the differences are more marked than the resemblances: instead of the *Threepenny* jazz band, a medium-sized orchestra without any jazz instruments; instead of a few brief passages for a beggarly chorus (mostly in unison), an almost Masonic role for a four-part chorus, whose interventions in the great monologue scene of Act 1 would be inconceivable without the example of Mozart's *The Magic Flute*.

As for the protagonist Severin, he is not only opposed in principle to his *Threepenny* counterpart Macheath, but is confronted by musical and histrionic challenges that any stage Macheath would have nightmares about: as the outraged voice of the dispossessed he has a full-blooded revenge aria that Verdi himself could have been proud of; and then, alone with his spirit-like partner Fennimore, he joins her in a duet whose long lyrical line and chromatically searching harmony would be more than just a heartache for the average Macheath and Polly.

Like Mendelssohn's music for *A Midsummer Night's Dream* or Grieg's for *Peer Gynt*, the *Silver Lake* score has a great deal to gain from concert performance, and perhaps even more than they have. But in Weill's case, to sacrifice the play is also to sacrifice the interplay of musical and dramatic forms. About that, Weill had more to say than even the Beethoven of *Egmont*; and just as Goethe should be a part of any complete performance of the *Egmont* music, so will Georg Kaiser make himself felt as a 'presence' in the Prom premiere of *The Silver Lake*.

Markus Stenz conducts the London Sinfonietta and a distinguished group of soloists in The Silver Lake *in Prom 3*

Top Juanita Lascarro
sings Fennimore
Above Markus Stenz

Right Design by
Caspar Neher of the
Police station scene
(1933)

Serial killers

Philip Hensher describes the eternal fascination of Berg's voluptuous *Lulu*

MURDEROUSLY INTENSE, dramatic to the lurid edge of pulp fiction and driven by a sense of lowering, implacable fate, *Lulu* has always counted among its listeners those who, acknowledging its mastery, would still rather not face its difficult, seductive world. Stravinsky spoke of its 'vast decadence', while some Berg scholars have frankly expressed their regret that he set Wedekind's bleakly inexorable tragedy to music rather than the fanciful Hauptmann play *Und Pippa tanzt* he seriously considered.

But those who surrender to this greatest of all twentieth-century operas soon find themselves under its spell. Its devotees quickly fall into a discussion of its smallest details – the way the Dr Schön love motif is constructed, or why Lulu tells Alwa she poisoned his mother. If, in most operas, the audience were told that every character were obsessed with the heroine, we might look at the comfortably-built soprano and suspend disbelief. Here it seems immediately credible, because of the beginnings of our own fascination; even if it isn't with Lulu, but with *Lulu*.

On the surface the opera seems concerned with a banal contemporary reality of night-clubs and brothels, of electric door-bells. Underneath, every listener feels the thrumming, urgent pulse of the immemorial values of murder and desire, and understands that those electric door-bells are the harbingers of fate. What

Berg brought to Wedekind's plays was a new voluptuousness, and what he added to Wedekind's unblinking vision was a sense of the sublime.

It's conceivable that an audience could watch the original plays and see only cruelty; no-one hears the unmistakable, sumptuous sound of the *Lulu* orchestra, or the fabulous, show-stopping virtuosity of the vocal writing, and hears anything but love, and a fascination which can't be denied, and can't, quite, be understood.

Virtuosity is at the heart of *Lulu*; not just the vertiginous thrill of its orchestra at full throttle, or the impossibly ravishing coloratura given to Lulu, which restores so much power and control to a figure who might otherwise be regarded as a victim. The profoundest virtuosity here is Berg's, producing from an astoundingly rigorous and symmetrical system, music which seems utterly natural, fresh and direct.

Nothing so perfectly carries out Schoenberg's instruction, when he wrote about the serial method in which it is written; 'one uses the system', he wrote, 'and then one writes music as before'. *Lulu* is emphatically not 'music as before'; but in its complete originality, it shares with the greatest masterpieces the mysterious, vital quality of music that has always been there, and never, quite, heard properly before.

Andrew Davis conducts Glyndebourne Festival Opera in a semi-staged performance of Berg's Lulu *in Prom 44*

Left Louise Brooks as Lulu in the film *Pandora's Box*

Above Portrait of Berg by Arnold Schoenberg

Top right Christine Schäfer

Paul Griffiths explores fifty states of music

Variations on America

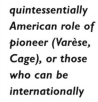

N OBODY TOLD ME that Variations on 'America' by Charles Ives would turn out to be based on the tune we all know as 'God Save the Queen'. In the United States, what you think will be different often proves the same.

And what you think will be the same ...

Take musical institutions. In the US, as in any European country, classical music is sustained in performance by symphony orchestras, concert halls, opera companies – but their support comes almost entirely from individual and corporate benefactors. This public art is private.

But that doesn't always affect what gets played. Even the Metropolitan Opera puts on Berg, Janáček and the

occasional new piece, and the big American orchestras probably do more contemporary music than their counterparts in Europe.

For instance, the New York Philharmonic shot off commissions hither and yon to celebrate its 150th birthday three seasons ago. Messiaen's immense late masterpiece *Éclairs sur l'au-delà* ... was one result.

Ned Rorem's Cor Anglais Concerto, to be heard at the Proms, was another. Rorem is the kind of American composer – urbane, distanced from theorising, sophisticatedly natural – who doesn't get played (or sung: he's a prolific songwriter) in Europe.

Yet he's not the only one or the only kind. It's strange that Milton Babbitt still isn't recognised much beyond the American north-east coast as being – with Haydn, Beethoven and Chabrier – one of music's great humorists.

The American composers whose music most readily crosses the Atlantic tend to be those who take America as their subject (Ives, Copland), those who take on the

quintessentially American role of pioneer (Varèse, Cage), or those who can be internationally understood because they speak Basic Music (Glass).

Elliott Carter is an exception – a European composer, perhaps, born in the wrong place. There he was in Chicago a couple of years ago, regretting that these days his music couldn't be played by American orchestras, because they couldn't give it sufficient rehearsal time.

This is where America's musical private enterprise starts to cause problems. The abundance of premieres disguises a dearth of music that doesn't fit established patterns.

Last season the Meet the Composer programme, funded by the National Endowment for the Arts (the US Arts Council) to encourage contacts between composers and audiences, announced successful encounters in all but two states: Wyoming and Arkansas. Where is it the President comes from?

Right (clockwise from top left)
George Gershwin
Aaron Copland
Charles Ives
Edgard Varèse

Left Leonard Slatkin conducts Ives, Copland, Adams and Ellington in Prom 20

All Americans are immigrants. All American music is immigrant music.

Immigrants remember.

Immigrants forget.

Immigrants remember. Hence the symphony orchestras, concert halls, opera companies, and hence too the long tradition of aspiration to anything perceived as a European ideal.

Example: the great American symphony. Genre initiated by Dvořák in 1893 and still going strong.

Immigrants forget. Hence the possibility of starting again, the lightness of history.

Example: Varèse's Amériques, *a title he chose as 'symbolic of discoveries – new worlds on earth, in the sky, or in the minds of men'.*

Further example: the music of Steve Reich, developing a whole new musical culture from the ground up.

Immigrants remember and they forget, so that they have to patch their memories with those of

other people. Hence, for instance, jazz.

History is what distinguishes culture from entertainment. Light in history, American music once easily confused the two.

Leonard Bernstein is the classic case, author in the 1950s of *West Side Story* and symphonies.

In Europe, you had to choose. In Europe, Bernstein meant *West Side Story.*

This has changed. Now, especially in America, entertainment is endowing itself with history.

Example: Bernstein recording West Side Story *for Deutsche Grammophon.*

Further example: Broadway's 1990s diet of revivals. Carol Channing's

return in *Hello, Dolly!* may not be culture but sure is living history.

American culture, to get back to that, was founded by people leaving behind seventeenth-century or eighteenth-century or nineteenth-century European culture. Now we in Europe too are moving on. Time is our Atlantic.

So US means us.

Maybe this is why American music has been so dominant since the First World War.

It wasn't so before. Impossible moment: Mahler conducting Ives's *Unanswered Question* with the New York Philharmonic.

Musical America a century ago was behaving as if it were a peripheral (but rich) European country.

Examples: the founding of the Metropolitan Opera (1883), Carnegie Hall (1891) and the Chicago Symphony Orchestra (also 1891), and the visits of Dvořák and Tchaikovsky.

Further examples: the symphonies of John Knowles Paine, the piano music of Edward

Top left
Leonard Bernstein

Centre left
John Adams

Above
London Adventist Chorale sing Gospel music and spirituals in Prom 19

MacDowell, the songs of Amy Beach.

Deeper back, though, there were stirrings of independence from Europe.

Examples: the untutored Anthony Philip Heinrich's collection The Dawning of Music in Kentucky *(1820) and the music of Louis Moreau Gottschalk.*

Here were ancestors awaiting Ives and Cage.

Here too in the nineteenth century is the start of the lasting antithesis between the great forgetters (Heinrich, Cage, Glass) and the great rememberers (MacDowell, Carter, Harbison).

Top right Carnegie Hall

Below Duke Ellington

Remembering and forgetting: hence the tumbling variety of popular music produced in the great American cities by the tumbling together of people of African, Jewish, Mediterranean and northern European descent. Not just ragtime, jazz, blues and gospel music but also music in such originally European forms as the parlour song, march, social dance and hymn, all transformed.

Hence Ives, a great forgetter (of European rules) who was also a great rememberer (of the American vernacular of his boyhood).

Hence too such sophisticated syntheses as Duke Ellington's or George Gershwin's.

Ives exemplifies as well the new American cultural economy. Culture has virtually no financial support from the state. Performers can get support from their audiences, but composers have to fend for themselves. Ives set up an insurance business.

Not many composers have taken that route. The more obvious way for composers to earn a living is by selling the skills they have as composers, either by writing commercial music or by teaching.

Hence the phenomenon of the university composer – a phenomenon that has grown to be international as part of the Americanisation of cultural life.

The university becomes, like a Renaissance court, a centre of creation and performance set apart from the bulk of society.

If serious music isn't given any economic privileges to compensate for its labour-intensiveness, its only resort is to claim the prerogative of an academic discipline.

Culture separates itself from entertainment only by becoming study.

Compositional method becomes inevitable. Otherwise there's nothing to teach.

And music thrives in the universities, colleges and conservatories. This is one great irony of American musical life, that so many wonderful musicians (composers, instru-mentalists, singers) are wonderfully trained for functions in society that do not exist.

Placed in the market, music also survives by mechanisation. Edison. Muzak. The grand pianola music of Conlon Nancarrow. The systematic rhythmic processes of Reich.

American music is America-shaped: not a landmass but a multifarious web of things and places – Ives, Varèse, Ellington, the New York Philharmonic – linked by filaments of air.

Manuel de Falla

Poul Ruders

Sir Malcolm Arnold

Joaquín Rodrigo

Igor Stravinsky

Sir Arnold Bax

Carl Nielsen

Jean Sibelius

Kevin Volans

John Adams

Sir Peter Maxwell Davies

Tan Dun

Sir Edward Elgar

Witold Lutoslawski

Geoffrey Burgon

Charles Ives

For information about
any of our composers
please contact...
The Promotions Department
Chester Music/Novello & Company
8-9 Frith Street
London WIV 5TZ
Telephone: 0171-434 0066
Fax: 0171-287 6329

New music, classic music...
we are honoured to publish works by these composers,
all of whom are featured in this year's
BBC Promenade Concerts

CHESTER MUSIC

Chester Music
Established 1860
Novello & Company
Established 1830
G Schirmer/AMP
Established 1861
Edition Wilhelm Hansen
Established 1857
Edwin Ashdown
Established 1882
Unión Musical Ediciones
Established 1900
The Music Sales Group
Bringing you the world's best music

Agreeing to disagree

Nick Kimberley explores the ambiguities of the concerto form and welcomes seven examples new to the Proms

Above
BBC Symphony Orchestra

Left
Poul Ruders working on *Concerto in Pieces*

T O AGREE, to contend or dispute? The *Shorter Oxford English Dictionary* derives the word 'concerto' from the Italian *concertare*, 'to bring into agreement'. Yet the same dictionary finds the origin of the word 'concertation' in the earlier, Latin form of *concertare*, meaning 'to contend or dispute together'. There, etymologically encapsulated, is the drama of the concerto form: soloist and orchestra working towards a common goal, yet with the soloist battling for supremacy.

That drama continues to entice composers, as evidenced by the number of new and recent concertos in this year's Proms. In the words of John Woolrich, whose Oboe Concerto receives its premiere, 'The concerto, like the symphony, is one of those forms that emerge from tonal language. As composers, we have to find a new way of thinking about it, of renewing that image of one versus the many, the theatrical power of the individual voice against the mass'.

The seven concertos show composers taking very different approaches to the form's inherent drama. Poul Ruders, born in Denmark in 1949, is a brilliant orchestrator, his music based, in the words of David

DORLING KINDERSLEY

Fanning, on 'fluid transitions, dramatic confrontation and energy'. All three characteristics are to the fore in his *Concerto in Pieces* (a BBC commission, receiving its London premiere), which the composer calls 'a double celebration'. Originally commissioned to mark the fiftieth birthday of Britten's *Young Person's Guide to the Orchestra* (1946), it was brought forward so as to become part of 1995's tercentenary celebrations of Purcell, whose music provided Britten with the germ for his *Guide*, and it had a hugely successful premiere at the BBC's 'Music Live 95' in Birmingham last year.

A snatch of Purcell is the starting-point for Ruders's work too, but as the composer admits, 'It would have been suicidal to have chosen the same Purcell theme as Britten, so I chose the fast and furious Witches' Chorus from *Dido and Aeneas*. I wanted to show the various faces of the modern symphony orchestra – how you can change its nature by doublings, blendings and so on. That's why it's "in pieces", suggesting variations and combinations.'

Ruders provides an unexpected analogy to describe the workings of his piece: 'The process of listening to *Concerto in Pieces* is like a stroll through a hall of distorting mirrors: you start out with the Purcell theme

Clockwise, left to right

Christian Lindberg premieres Dominic Muldowney's Trombone Concerto in Prom 4; Dominic Muldowney; Tony Hancock

totally recognisable, then everything becomes distorted, although it's the same original "walking by". Then I end with a pizzicato transition to take the theme back to near-recognisability. There *is* some solo writing, but mostly it's a concerto for orchestra, with the mocking spirit of the Witches' Chorus hovering behind every variation. It's boisterous, flamboyant, a real virtuoso piece: perfect for the Last Night of the Proms!'.

If Ruders fêtes Purcell and Britten, Dominic Muldowney's Trombone Concerto celebrates a no less British figure. Muldowney, born in 1952, has been Musical Director of London's Royal National Theatre since 1981, and his music displays a vivid theatricality, supported by a thoroughgoing empathy with the work of Brecht, Weill and Eisler. Showing a Brechtian willingness to wrongfoot the listener, Muldowney says of his concerto, 'The trombone carries the baggage of being both comic and tragic, capable of being a clown, blowing a raspberry, yet consistently used over the past

few centuries at moments of great solemnity. I wanted to enter that dangerous world where something serious dissolves into hilarity, or vice versa – like those stories of comedians dying on stage. In fact, it was Tony Hancock who kept on tapping my skull as I was writing it, and I've dedicated the piece to his memory'. The theme tune from Hancock's radio and television show is deeply embedded in the national consciousness. In Muldowney's hands, the first six notes of the tune generate a fugue from which the whole concerto grows. 'It starts with a cadenza, just like a comic coming on stage and telling a one-liner.'

Where Muldowney hears the trombone blowing a raspberry, others approach their concertos with no less oral, although perhaps more familiar images in mind. John Woolrich suggests that the oboe for which he has provided his concerto 'can do fantastic ornamental filigrees, but it sounds most characteristic if it's

singing'.

The American composer Ned Rorem agrees: 'Every instrument strives for the condition of the human voice'. A student in the 1940s of Virgil Thomson and Aaron Copland, he went on to become one of the United States' most accomplished art-song composers, as well as a hedonist and diarist of some indiscretion. His concerto receiving its London premiere at the Proms is for English horn – not a prominent player in concerto history. Rorem notes, 'It's interesting that the English call it cor anglais. Everyone else calls it English horn'. For Rorem, 'It's a very seductive instrument with all the mean, tight qualities of the oboe, but also the languorous, luscious sounds of a bassoon. It has a bigger range than an oboe, not only of notes, but of emotion'. Yet Rorem concedes, 'The English horn can so quickly get lost, so I was continually anxious about its not being drowned. I use fewer instruments as I get older anyway. I don't morally approve of percussion, for example. It's like too many

JOSH MITCHELL CHRIS LEE MALCOLM CROWTHERS HANYA CHLALA MARCO BORGGREVE GAUTIER DEBLONDE

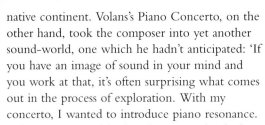

Clockwise, left to right
Netherlands Wind
Ensemble;
Kevin Volans;
Peter Donohoe gives
the UK premiere of
Kevin Volans's Piano
Concerto in Prom 43

Above
Nicholas Daniel
premieres
John Woolrich's Oboe
Concerto in Prom 33

Left
John Woolrich

earrings – its effect is in inverse proportion to its use'.

John Woolrich, born in 1954, is best known for his works for smaller ensembles: indeed, he is co-founder of the Composers' Ensemble, a valuable resource since its inception in 1989. Widely experienced in chamber music, Woolrich, like Rorem, grappled with problems of balance in writing his Oboe Concerto: 'There are plenty of instruments I don't feel I can write naturally for, but with the oboe, a door suddenly opened into my imagination. It's a very fragile voice, but I didn't want to scale the orchestra down. I wanted an Albert Hall-sized orchestra. Then I looked at Mozart, and it was as if a flood of light came down from heaven. The way to write is not virtuosically, because it doesn't always sound very good. I decided to write a piece pitting the fragility of the oboe against a massive and mechanical orchestra – a fragile thing in a dark, cold world'.

The South African composer Kevin Volans studied with Stockhausen in the 1970s, although his music subsequently developed in quite different directions, often achieving a rapprochement with the music of his native continent. Volans's Piano Concerto, on the other hand, took the composer into yet another sound-world, one which he hadn't anticipated: 'If you have an image of sound in your mind and you work at that, it's often surprising what comes out in the process of exploration. With my concerto, I wanted to introduce piano resonance. A lot of piano music of the last thirty years has had very little to do with resonance. But it's difficult to explore resonance without getting into nineteenth-century harmony, and the piece *does* have Romantic connotations, even though I didn't have that in mind'.

Volans admits that his view of music generally runs counter to nineteenth-century notions of the concerto: 'I firmly believe that in late twentieth-century music, rather like in Matisse, everything is foreground, rather than foreground and background. It was a problem to have a single instrument playing against a large group, and not have the group sound like background' – a problem complicated by the fact that the group for which the piece was written was the Netherlands Wind Ensemble, 'and the wind ensemble is very loud, much more powerful than a symphony orchestra'.

Many composers use titles as a kind of suggestive

aid to draw the listener into their work. None deploys titles more poetically than Henri Dutilleux, one of France's most distinguished composers this century and, at the age of eighty, still a potent force in that country's culture. Writing of his violin concerto, which he calls *L'Arbre des songes* ('Tree of Dreams'), Dutilleux has suggested that: 'All in all the piece grows somewhat like a tree, for the constant multiplication and renewal of its branches is the lyrical essence of the tree'. At the Proms the piece will

be conducted by Yan Pascal Tortelier, who confirms that 'Dutilleux's titles are not merely superficially attractive, they're very much part of his creative process. His scores are a little like paintings, and his work is somewhat in the vein of the French Impressionists.'

Tortelier's father, the great cellist Paul Tortelier, was a close friend of Dutilleux's from the days when they were students together in Paris in the 1930s. When Tortelier *fils* came to conduct the music of Dutilleux about ten years ago, he felt that the composer was 'almost a member of the family'. In his view, 'Dutilleux has been central to musical life in France for several decades, but he was little known abroad until quite recently. There are some extraordinary colours in the violin concerto that are not always there in his music. Maybe that is something to do with the fact that Isaac Stern [who premiered the work, and has since recorded it] is such a lyrical and warm player'.

Tortelier suggests that Dutilleux used his soloist, Isaac Stern, almost as an instrument whose exact sonorities dictated the nature of the concerto. For Oliver Knussen, the horn-player Barry Tuckwell was no less instrumental (so to speak) in shaping his thoughts about his Horn Concerto, which Tuckwell premiered in Japan in 1994 (the score was revised in 1995). Knussen says 'The music began as a grateful response to more than thirty years of hearing Barry Tuckwell play'.

Asked to write a piece to be performed in Tokyo's Suntory Hall, Knussen felt that 'the subtle colour-gradations, wide dynamic range and what might be termed "spatial" characteristics of the horn sound-world would be heard to ideal effect in that room. Thoughts of this nature eventually led to the conception of a predominantly lyrical work which employs a large orchestra (including two sets of timpani) in a very economical manner'.

Here, then, Knussen balances the elements which, for all these composers, contribute to the special drama of the concerto form: the unique qualities of the player, and of their instrument; the acoustic properties of the hall (and few have a character more personal than the Royal Albert Hall); and, of course, the nature of the orchestra itself. The history of music this century may at times have seemed to leave the orchestra, as Poul Ruders's title suggests, 'in pieces' but, whether it invokes musical agreement or disputation, the concerto retains its ability to bring those pieces back together, to make it whole and, not least important, to make it new.

Left
Henri Dutilleux with the score of his Violin Concerto

Bottom left
Olivier Charlier plays *L'Arbre des songes* in Prom 69

Below
Oliver Knussen

Below Barry Tuckwell gives the London premiere of Knussen's Horn Concerto

TRANSART (UK) LTD MALCOLM CROWTHERS HANYA CHLALA

KNOWLEDGE, RANGE, SERVICE...

CLASSICALLY ORCHESTRATED

KNOW HMV • KNOW MUSIC

150 OXFORD STREET, LONDON W1 • 363 OXFORD STREET, LONDON W1
MANCHESTER • OXFORD • BIRMINGHAM • LEEDS • LIVERPOOL • TROCADERO
KINGSTON • SOUTHAMPTON • EDINBURGH • RICHMOND • BRIGHTON
GLASGOW, SAUCHIEHALL STREET • GLASGOW, ARGYLE STREET • READING
CHESTER • BATH • BRENT CROSS • CROYDON • CHELTENHAM • IPSWICH

BOOTHROYD STUART MERIDIAN©

Expertise

Meridian Audio is one of the world's leading companies making audio systems – everything from exceptional CD players to the most advanced digital surround sound systems.

Throughout the 80's Meridian pioneered the development of digital sound for the home – in the 90's we have built on this expertise to become one of the leading manufacturers of surround sound systems.

Unlike others, we not only design and make our own products but write the software which controls them.
As a result, all our products are designed as part of a matching system which is easy to use and can always be up to date.

Whether you want to listen to your music in stereo or watch a movie with eight channel surround sound, we make what you need now – and we always will.

Call or fax us for a brochure or visit our web page for the whole picture.

Meridian Audio Limited

Stonehill, Stukeley Meadows,
Huntingdon, Cambridgeshire PE18 6ED
Tel **44** (0)1480 52144 Fax **44** (0)1480 459934
http://www.meridian.co.uk

Meridian America Inc

3800 Camp Creek Parkway, Building 2400,
Suite 112, Atlanta, GA 30331
Tel (404) 344 7111 Fax (404) 346 7111

" One doesn't refuse a Prom; it's like turning down an audience with the Queen "

Early arrivals

Lindsay Kemp introduces period-instrument performers from abroad

EARLY MUSIC is no newcomer to the Proms; even in the first few seasons there was Handel and Bach aplenty. But while we cannot know exactly what Mr Lempriere Pringle sounded like singing 'O ruddier than the cherry' from *Acis and Galatea* in 1896, we can be pretty sure that the result bore little resemblance to most modern-day performances of the same music. Indeed, early music in the 1990s does not even sound much like it did thirty years ago, since when there has been a dramatic acceleration of a process not completely unknown in Pringle's day, but which is now firmly centre-stage. 'Authentic', 'historically aware', 'lentils-and-sandals' – call it what you will – the performance of music from before 1800 has been transformed by the rise of players and singers using instruments and techniques appropriate to the period.

Britain can take much of the credit. The strength of this country's period orchestras and choirs is well attested at this year's Proms by the presence with their respective ensembles of Trevor Pinnock, John Eliot Gardiner and Ivor Bolton, all of whom have a long history of engagements abroad. But while audiences from Seville to Sydney have had plenty of opportunities to experience the British early-music sound, the opposite has not been true. Partly for financial reasons but partly also, one suspects, from

sheer complacency, visits to this country by top-rate period orchestras and choirs from abroad remain infrequent. And even though the Proms have long been among the most welcoming of hosts for foreign ensembles of all kinds, even they have rarely managed more than one overseas early-music group per season.

This year, however, things are different. For the first time, four distinguished conductors from Europe will be appearing at the Proms – three of them with the early-music ensembles they themselves founded – providing a remarkable opportunity for the large audiences of the Albert Hall to experience something new and perhaps a little exotic.

For British audiences, the most familiar of this year's visitors are probably the American William Christie and his talented France-based group of singers and players, Les Arts Florissants. Together they have performed in Britain many times, including at a late-night concert in the 1984 Proms. On that occasion they appeared in a Chelsea church in music by Charpentier (from one of whose works they take their name), but their return sees them performing music by Handel – his sparkling musical drama *Semele* – and brings them for the first time to the Albert Hall, where they have a rare chance to entertain a really

Left William Christie

Right George Frideric Handel

large audience with their unfailing polish and dramatic energy.

Christie admits to finding the prospect 'a bit daunting'. But, he says, 'one doesn't refuse a Prom; it's like turning down an audience with the Queen. All my colleagues who have performed there have come away talking about the audience and the atmosphere, which is so heady and exciting, so I'm looking forward to it very much. The band's going to be pretty big and there's a lot of wonderful chorus work, so we should fill the place. I adore conducting Handel – I love his vocality – and *Semele* is real Proms fare, a fluffy, wonderful piece all about sex and money. It's kind of Joan Collins-y!'.

Christie is one of the first among a growing number of conductors whose keen dramatic instincts have helped to increase public interest in Baroque opera in recent years. Another is the Belgian René Jacobs, whose superb recording of Handel's *Julius Caesar* five years ago was hailed as 'one of the most important Handel recordings of the century'. This year he makes his Prom debut, appearing with Britain's own Orchestra of the Age of Enlightenment in a Bach-Handel programme that will include excerpts from

> ### "Semele *is real Proms fare, a fluffy, wonderful piece all about sex and money. It's kind of Joan Collins-y!*"

Handel's great masterpiece. Note the word 'excerpts': this will not be just a compilation of the opera's best tunes, but a sequence in which Spanish soprano María Bayo and German counter-tenor Andreas Scholl will sing a selection of arias with their preceding recitatives.

Jacobs, who originally made his own name as a counter-tenor with a highly individual interpretative style, has always believed in the importance of recitative. 'I don't like it if you take Handel arias totally out of context', he explains. 'If there is no recitative, there is no feeling for the drama. Maybe it works for a recording, but when I do them in concert there will be recitatives.'

Jacobs also believes that including the recitatives will help him overcome any difficulties there might be in bringing the music to life in such a large venue. 'I have good and bad memories of playing in big halls, but really it depends on how you play. It's one of the most difficult but also one of the most rewarding things for a musician to be able to fill a big hall. With a small orchestra in there, everybody plays as if their life is depending on it.'

Jacobs's concert will end with Bach's *Magnificat*, but it's an all-Bach programme which sees the Proms debut of another Belgian conductor, Philippe Herreweghe. Last year Herreweghe celebrated the twenty-fifth anniversary of his choir, the Collegium Vocale of

Semele - *The famous aria 'Where'er you walk' apart, performances of* Semele *are surprisingly rare, despite the fact that it is among Handel's most admired works.* Confusion over just what sort of piece it is has not helped. It was first performed in London in 1744 'after the manner of an oratorio' (ie unstaged), but even those listeners who did not know that Congreve's forty-year-old libretto was originally conceived for an opera could have seen that this was a stage-work in disguise. The story comes from Ovid, and tells of the love of Jupiter, chief of the gods, for the flighty Theban princess Semele, whose ambitious desire for immortality eventually leads to her downfall. The work is frank in its depiction of sensual love, but for all that one contemporary described it as 'bawdy' Semele *is a witty and sophisticated piece which, in its sexy title-role, includes one of the most fascinating of Handel's many vivid female characterisations.*

William Christie directs Les Arts Florissants in Handel's Semele *in Prom 21*

Ghent, and although he has since formed other groups to perform choral music ranging from Palestrina to Schoenberg, Bach has always remained at the centre of his work with the group he founded in his home town. Early on, they took part in the famous complete Bach cantata recording cycle with Gustav Leonhardt, and since then they have made their own exquisitely musical recordings of the major Bach choral works.

For the Prom, Herreweghe naturally wants to show their experience to best advantage: 'As we don't come to London very often, we're trying to make a programme which will show the different qualities of the choir. So we have a motet, a cantata and the Mass in G minor, which has a lot of choruses in it, more than in a cantata'. This last is one of Bach's four charming 'short Masses', still heard surprisingly rarely today, but something of a cause for Herreweghe. 'They are all wonderful and the choir love to sing them because it's fantastic music. I don't understand at all why they are not performed, except that for amateur choirs they are perhaps a little more difficult than the B minor Mass. It's very strange.'

Our last early-music visitor, like our first, has been to the Proms before. Frans Brüggen, who as a brilliantly inventive recorder virtuoso was at the forefront of the period-instrument movement back in the 1960s, was here only three years ago for a typically original performance of Beethoven's 'Choral' Symphony with the Orchestra of the Age of Enlightenment. This time he is back, but bringing for the first time his own band, the Orchestra of the Eighteenth Century. Or rather, he is back with two bands: for the Beethoven Violin Concerto (for which the soloist is the German Thomas Zehetmair) the orchestra will use one set of 'Classical' instruments, and another set of lower-pitched 'Baroque' ones for a suite of dances from Rameau's *opéra-ballet, Les Fêtes d'Hébé.*

Brüggen now conducts many ensembles, but his work with the Orchestra of the Eighteenth Century is still special. 'Our principles have not changed', he says. 'We still work for three month-long periods per year, and these are all blocked off five years in advance, so everybody knows when to appear. We have nineteen nationalities and we're a real bunch of friends.' There is also a policy of not repeating a piece from one work-period to another, which ought to help Brüggen achieve his ambition for this Prom: 'As always, one hopes that the audience will experience the concert, not as a concert of "new" music exactly, but as the premiere of something. I hope we can achieve that first performance experience'.

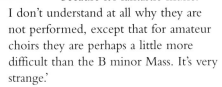

When it comes to light classical music, we're on your wavelength.

BBC Radio 2 and the BBC Concert Orchestra are set to bring you some of the most outstanding light classical music you'll hear this year.

The BBC Concert Orchestra will be performing at the Harrogate, Salisbury, Bury St Edmunds, Portsmouth, Peterborough, Exeter, Windsor, Bournemouth, Henley, Chichester and Llandudno music festivals.

Radio 2 will bring you coverage of many of these concerts as well as a wide selection of other live music by the BBC Concert Orchestra on 'Friday Night is Music Night' and also in gala and showcase concert programmes throughout 1996.

So, if you love live music, don't forget to tune in.

BBC
Concert Orchestra

COMMITTED TO LIVE MUSIC

BBC RADIO **2** 88-91 FM

CHANDOS

Chandos are proud to support our Exclusive Artists

BBC
Philharmonic

Richard
Hickox

Yan Pascal
Tortelier

Louis
Lortie

Matthias
Bamert

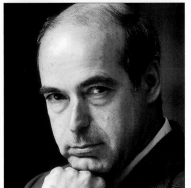

Chandos Records Ltd, Chandos House, Commerce Way, Colchester, Essex CO2 8HQ

Pursuing novelty

Left
The BBC Symphony
Orchestra and Chorus
at the 1994 Proms

From top
Alfred Schnittke
Sir Michael Tippett
Mark-Anthony Turnage

Gavin Thomas looks at the BBC's contribution to new music

IT WAS MARGARET THATCHER, back in the 1980s, who decisively pushed arts funding into the political spotlight. For better or worse, the attitudes she fostered are still very much with us: against a downward spiral of government funding for arts organisations, the BBC orchestras, as well as their independent colleagues, have had to rationalise and rethink – to find a way, as Hugh Macdonald, Chief Producer of the BBC Scottish Symphony Orchestra, puts it, 'to reconcile our mission to be challenging with the need to balance the books'.

So where does this leave the promotion of new and financially demanding music? The corporation's flagship, the BBC Symphony Orchestra, continues in collaboration with the Proms and Radio 3 to commission some thirteen works a year; but, as Chief Producer Ann McKay explains, with a growing concern to present such new pieces in a way which makes them accessible to the widest possible audience.

Not that this means any lessening of the orchestra's famously pioneering spirit. The mission remains unchanged: to provide a platform not only for Britain's brightest talents but also, as McKay says, for 'those major international figures who are too rarely heard in this country, and also those significant but unfashionable composers who might otherwise not receive a hearing'.

It's this desire to explore unknown territory which is crucial to the work of the BBC orchestras. McKay cites the case of Tippett, a composer who received unswerving support from the BBC at a time when his reputation was far from secure. Fittingly, the BBC SO

will be giving the Prom premiere of what the composer says is his last major work. *The Rose Lake*, a haunting orchestral 'song without words', was inspired by the changing colours of a Senegalese lake, a vision translated by Tippett into a gloriously lyrical and affirmative end to a lifetime of outstanding creative achievement.

Also making a welcome Prom debut is *Your Rockaby*, written by Mark-Anthony Turnage for Martin Robertson and the BBC SO. Turnage is a much younger British composer who shares Tippett's vigorous eclecticism, drawing in this piece for saxophone and orchestra on a high-octane cocktail of bluesy schmaltz and precipitous rhythmic frenzy before finally unwinding into a spooky concluding lullaby.

There's also a first Prom performance for Schnittke's colourful *Dead Souls* suite, arranged by Gennady Rozhdestvensky (himself a former Chief Conductor of the BBC SO) from Schnittke's music to Michail Schweizer's 1983 film, one of the sixty-odd film scores which its composer penned to support himself during the Communist era.

One new face this season is that of Siegfried Matthus, who is perhaps best known in his native Germany as an opera composer, but who has also written an important series of concertos, of which *Der Wald* ('The Forest'), for timpani and reduced orchestra, is the sixth. The title alludes both to the nature-worship of German Romanticism and to the twentieth century's betrayal of those ideals, mirrored musically by evoking and then destroying Romantic images, before returning to the nostalgic visions of the

STP PHOTOGRAPHY KATIE VANDYCK ALEX VON KOETTLITZ EASTPRESS OY ERIC THORBURN JÖRG LANDSBERG

beginning of the piece, 'offered like an open question to the future'.

Add to these the world premiere of a BBC-commissioned concerto for oboe by John Woolrich, plus the London premiere of Poul Ruders's *Concerto in Pieces*, and one can only conclude that the BBC SO has no intention of relinquishing its position at the forefront of the international new music scene.

For the BBC's three regional orchestras, the challenge is not only to forge a national and international presence, but also to provide a platform for local talent, both established and up-and-coming. The two new works which the BBC National Orchestra of Wales will be bringing to the Proms this year are both by composers with strong links to the region. Born in 1963, John Pickard is one of the latest in a long line of composers to have been brought forward by a BBC commission. *The Flight of Icarus*, a compelling blend of whirlwind orchestral virtuosity and large-scale symphonic thinking, was written for the BBC NOW in 1990, since when it has featured regularly in the orchestra's repertoire. Pickard gives a contemporary twist to the classic myth of Icarus's doomed flight, relating it to man's explorations of space, both triumphant and disastrous – a parable, argues the composer, for the idea that 'all human endeavour must, from time to time, generate catastrophe, and our response to this is a test of our humanity'.

Like Pickard, the work of Anthony Powers effects a distinctive marriage of modernism and tradition, the one enriching the other, expressed in music of vivid colours and generous expressive range. Typical in this respect was the evocative nature-painting of his most recent BBC NOW commission, the landscape-inspired symphonic poem *Terrain* (1993), though his new Symphony, Powers suggests, will be a more abstract piece in four movements, concerning 'the narrative journeys of different kinds of music' which are gradually fused as the work progresses.

The BBC Scottish Symphony Orchestra and the Manchester-based BBC Philharmonic have also established strong links with composers born or living in their areas, though their contributions to this season's Proms in fact have a distinctly international flavour. The Chinese-born, American-based composer Tan Dun was discovered by the BBC Scottish SO during a mini-festival of music from the People's Republic held in Glasgow in 1988. Sensing Tan's star potential, the orchestra immediately commissioned a piece from him, *Orchestral Theatre I: Xun*, and subsequently appointed him Associate Composer/Conductor.

They will be bringing two new Tan Dun works to the Proms. *On Taoism*, whose exotic blend of Western avant-garde sonorities and Eastern ritual was, Tan says, 'inspired by the spiritual vibrations from my childhood', explores 'sound in many dimensions: microtonal, swimming among frequencies, expanding timbres as the

Top, clockwise from left The BBC National Orchestra of Wales with Tadaaki Otaka, who conducts Anthony Powers's Symphony in Prom 66; John Pickard; Mark Wigglesworth, Music Director of BBC NOW, who conducts *The Flight of Icarus* in Prom 14

Centre
Osmo Vänskä conducts Detlev Glanert's Third Symphony in Prom 46

Below, clockwise from right
Anthony Powers; Tan Dun directs two of his works in Prom 23; Detlev Glanert

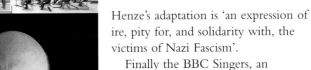

ink of calligraphy spreads in rice paper'. Also receiving a belated Prom premiere is *Orchestral Theatre II: Re*, which was to have featured in last year's season until a power cut forced the concert to be abandoned.

A second international strand is supplied by the premiere of a new work from a leading younger German composer, Detlev Glanert, whose music makes conscious reference back to composers such as Mahler and, especially, Berg, in an attempt to forge progressive links between past and present – 'to find a new way of using the power of old symbols'. Glanert's piece will, its composer says, be in the nature of 'a little symphony', though his belief that 'a symphony of today can only be a discussion of the symphonies of yesterday' promises to set it somewhat apart from Anthony Powers's more direct exploration of the same agenda.

Continuing the German theme, the BBC Philharmonic will be presenting the UK premiere of a work by Glanert's former teacher, Hans Werner Henze, whose most recent orchestral score is an 'orchestration and free adaptation' of movements from Hartmann's piano sonata, *27 April 1945*, written after its composer had witnessed the transportation of detainees to the Nazi concentration camp at Dachau. Quoting both from Jewish folk music and workers' songs,

Henze's adaptation is 'an expression of ire, pity for, and solidarity with, the victims of Nazi Fascism'.

Finally the BBC Singers, an ensemble which, in parallel with the BBC Symphony Orchestra, has established itself at the forefront of the international new music scene. If the process of commissioning new works can be an uncertain business at the best of times, the BBC Singers have arguably as successful a track record as any group in the world. They've also shown a praiseworthy ability to identify those significant artists whose music (one remembers the case of Tippett) is perhaps initially too challenging to withstand the hurly-burly of the market-place.

In their own late-night programme two works commissioned for their seventieth-anniversary season – Andrew Simpson's *The Hollow Hills* and James MacMillan's *Màiri* – will receive another hearing. Simpson wrote his own text for *The Hollow Hills*, a dramatic scene based on King Arthur and the Knights of the Round Table, while MacMillan's *Màiri* adapts an elegy by the nineteenth-century Gaelic writer Ewan Maccoll. These two small choral pieces show further evidence of the extraordinary range of work we owe to the BBC. Long may its enlightened policy continue.

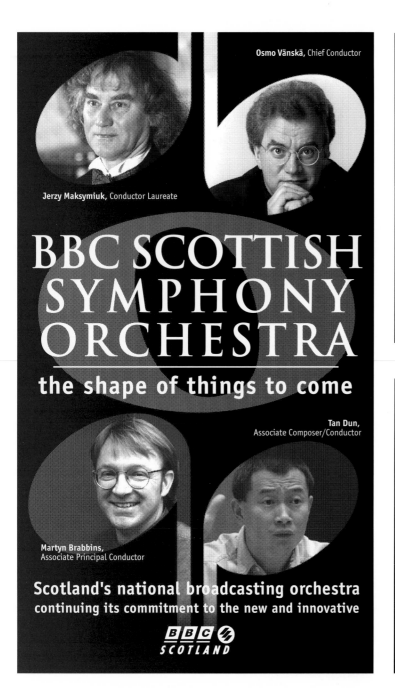

HALIFAX BUILDING

SOCIETY

IS PROUD TO

SUPPORT THE

1996 PROMS

HALIFAX

Visitors from afar

Matías Tarnopolsky previews six overseas orchestras appearing at the Proms

Berlin Philharmonic Orchestra

Proms 50 and 51

THE UNEARTHLY SILENCE that followed the momentous performance of Mahler's Ninth by Claudio Abbado and the Berlin Philharmonic at the Proms two years ago was one of the most memorable moments in the 100th season. The orchestra and conductor are in demand all over the world, but so overwhelmed were they by their reception at the Proms that they wish to return at regular intervals. This year Abbado brings Mahler's

mighty 'Resurrection' Symphony and an all-Brahms concert anticipating next year's centenary of his death. One of the world's most venerable musical institutions, the Berlin Philharmonic was founded in 1882, and its list of conductors includes Brahms, Grieg, Mahler, Richard Strauss, Tchaikovsky, Nikisch and Furtwängler. Herbert von Karajan dominated the orchestra for thirty-four years from 1955 in a partnership that left a decisive stamp on its sound and colour. Claudio Abbado succeeded Karajan in 1990, and in his six years as Artistic Director and Chief Conductor has established a close relationship with the orchestra. 'With them, I feel like I'm riding a thoroughbred – I try to convey the feeling of complete liberty and indicate with a few small gestures the direction we should take.' Abbado has broadened further the orchestra's horizons, with a new emphasis on contemporary music and international touring; he has also embarked on a major series of recordings which has been widely praised.

Chicago Symphony Orchestra

Proms 70 and 71

MAKING A WELCOME RETURN to the Proms after a seven-year absence is the Chicago Symphony Orchestra, under its Principal Conductor, Daniel Barenboim, and its Conductor

Above
Claudio Abbado

Left
Berlin Philharmonic
Orchestra

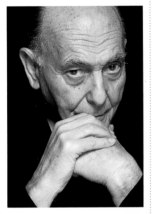

Laureate, Sir Georg Solti. One of this century's legendary musical figures, Sir Georg was Music Director of the Chicago Symphony from 1969 to 1991, though his association with the orchestra goes back even further. 'My love affair with the magnificent Chicago Symphony Orchestra began at the Ravinia Festival over forty years ago, in 1954', he says. 'It blossomed into the happiest musical marriage of my life and our two previous Prom appearances remain unforgettable highlights of my tenure as Music Director.' The great Argentinian-born Israeli conductor and pianist Daniel Barenboim succeeded Sir Georg Solti, becoming only the ninth Music Director in the orchestra's 105-year history. His tenure began with a series of the Mozart/Da Ponte operas, and appearances in the dual role of pianist and conductor. 'I am continually refreshed by their eagerness to re-examine music they have played many times and with enviable success. This is perhaps the greatest distinction of the Chicago Symphony Orchestra – it never rests on its past achievements, even though it is the toast of audiences throughout the world.' Barenboim has begun to record extensively with the orchestra, including contemporary music by Berio, Carter and Takemitsu. For this Prom, his first visit as a conductor since 1981, he brings Schoenberg's visionary Five Pieces for Orchestra and Bruckner's Eighth Symphony.

New York Philharmonic

Proms 40 and 41

THE ROSTER OF CONDUCTORS who have worked with the New York Philharmonic – the oldest orchestra in the United States, now in its 154th year – is impressive indeed: Tchaikovsky, Dvořák, Mahler (Music Director, 1909–11), Richard Strauss, Furtwängler, Toscanini (Music Director, 1929–36), Stravinsky, Koussevitzky and Walter. Recent Music

Directors have included Bernstein, Mehta and Boulez (under whom the orchestra made its first Prom appearance in 1975) and, since 1991, Kurt Masur.

Under Masur's directorship the New York Philharmonic was named 'Orchestra of the Year' at the 1993 Classical Music Awards, in recognition of its new initiatives and audience outreach efforts. Masur's association with the orchestra has been a fruitful one, and he is enthusiastic about playing to the Proms audiences. 'I am looking forward with great anticipation to presenting the English Horn Concerto by Ned Rorem, and I feel confident that you will enjoy the outstanding virtuosity of the orchestra in Richard Strauss's *Till Eulenspiegel* and will be impressed by the Russian sound in Tchaikovsky's Fifth Symphony', he says. As part of its 150th anniversary celebrations, the orchestra commissioned thirty-six new pieces over a ten-year period, building on its established commitment to new music (Dvořák's 'New World' Symphony counts amongst its early world premieres). Kurt Masur has also renewed the orchestra's recording tradition with recent releases including Brahms's *Requiem,* Mahler's Ninth, and music by Liszt and Kodály.

Oslo Philharmonic Orchestra

Proms 38 and 39

Norway's most celebrated ensemble returns to the Proms for the second year in succession. Their concert last season received rapturous acclaim in the Albert Hall and rave reviews in the press. In recent years the Oslo Philharmonic has established itself in the front rank of major international orchestras, a development due in large part to the conductor at its helm since 1979, Mariss Jansons. In 1994 the Oslo Philharmonic celebrated the seventy-fifth anniversary of its institution as a permanent independent body, though its origins date back to 1871, when Grieg was one of its founders and first conductors. Its interpretations of his music have received the highest acclaim and, appropriately, Grieg is one of the composers Jansons and the orchestra bring on this visit. They also champion the music of another compatriot, Alfred Janson, and tackle two peaks of the symphonic repertory, Mahler's Fifth and Dvořák's ever popular 'New World'. After the Proms the orchestra begins a major Far-East tour, and highlights of next year include a five-concert residency at the Vienna Musikverein. Under Jansons the Oslo Philharmonic has made a series of recordings, winning four Norwegian Grammy Awards and the Grand Prix du Disque.

Rotterdam Philharmonic Orchestra

Proms 62 and 63

The charismatic conductor Valery Gergiev makes a long-delayed Prom debut at the helm of the orchestra of which he is now Principal Conductor, the Rotterdam Philharmonic. Among the

Left
Mariss Jansons

Below left
Oslo Philharmonic
Orchestra

Below
Valery Gergiev

new developments under his leadership is the creation of the Rotterdam Philharmonic Gergiev Festival, which begins this September, and which includes chamber music and opera as well as orchestral concerts. Under him, the orchestra's performances of Debussy and Stravinsky (composers featured in their two Proms) have been especially praised, brought to life, he says, by 'the orchestra's very light, sunny sound and strong character'. Since 1918 the Rotterdam Philharmonic has been the musical heart of the city and a leading light on the European musical scene. The orchestra is renowned for its adventurous programming, a tradition which began under Eduard Flipse, Principal Conductor from 1930 to 1962. He steered the orchestra through the turbulent war years, when amongst the hardships it had to endure was having to rehearse at Rotterdam Zoo. Other principal conductors have included Franz-Paul Decker, Jean Fournet, Edo de Waart, David Zinman, James Conlon and Jeffrey Tate, while leading guest conductors include Bernard Haitink, Sir Simon Rattle, Michael Tilson Thomas and Gennady Rozhdestvensky.

Above
Rotterdam Philharmonic Orchestra

Top right
Mikhail Pletnev

Bottom right
Russian National Orchestra

Russian National Orchestra

Proms 24 and 26

BY FAR THE YOUNGEST of this season's featured visiting orchestras, the Russian National Orchestra was founded six years ago by the pianist and conductor Mikhail Pletnev, bringing together what he describes as 'a group of first-class musicians united for enthusiastic music-making'. Born from the sweeping reforms in the former Soviet

Union, it is the first entirely independent orchestra to exist in Russia since the Revolution. Its first concert, given in the Great Hall of the Moscow Conservatory in 1990, was a triumph, securing the orchestra an enthusiastic following at home. Its international career began the next year with concerts at the Ivo Pogorelich Festival in Germany, followed shortly afterwards by visits to the United States, Japan and Israel (the first Russian orchestra to perform there). Under Pletnev the orchestra has embarked on an ambitious recording programme which includes Tchaikovsky's *Manfred*, Rakhmaninov's Second Symphony and a selection of Russian overtures. Among the repertoire Pletnev and the orchestra bring to their first Proms are pieces by three Russian giants: Shostakovich, Prokofiev and Schnittke – music they carry in their blood.

Sir Frank Dicksee, *The Two Crowns*, 1900

Enjoy a Victorian crowning glory at the Tate thanks to BP.

Throughout the year BP enables the Tate to hang New Displays in each of its rooms, so you can discover much more of the Gallery's collection.

For instance, for the first time in nearly 20 years you can now see the picture voted most popular in the Royal Academy Exhibition in the last year of Victoria's glorious reign. Sir Frank Dicksee's allegory of a triumphal king being reminded of a higher purpose was immediately bought for the nation for £2,000 and hung in the recently opened Tate Gallery.

So thanks to BP, you can now see Dicksee's gorgeous colours and sumptuous richness for yourself. You'll find it's still a triumph of the painter's art today.

TateGallery Millbank, London SW1. Tel: 0171 887 8008. Open Mon-Sat 10am-5.50pm, Sunday 2pm-5.50pm.

When to book your concerts

Until Monday 10 June the ONLY way to book tickets from the full range of concerts in the Proms is by using the booking form on page 109 of this guide.

Postal and Fax Bookings
Begin on Monday 13 May.

All forms received before the official booking period opens will be date stamped Monday 13 May.

Fax Bookings
Please note that any faxes received before postal and fax booking opens will be date stamped Monday 13 May. Fax 0171 584 1406.

Telephone Bookings
Begin on Monday 10 June. Call 0171 589 8212 9.00am – 9.00pm daily.

Personal Bookings
Begin on Monday 10 June. Visit the Royal Albert Hall Ticket Shop at Door 7. Open 9.00am – 9.00pm daily.

Important information on Priority Orders

For orders received between 13 May and 10 June, priority will be given to the following:

• Season Tickets

• All-In Tickets

• Concerts in Price Codes A and D

• Concerts in Price Codes B and C, provided you have also booked at least ONE concert in Price Code A.

Those wishing to book for concerts in Price Codes B and C, but who do not wish to book also for a concert in Price Code A, will have their orders dealt with once the Priority Orders have been fulfilled but before general booking opens on 10 June.

For information on tickets for the Last Night, please see page 116.

By the time general booking opens on 10 June, many of the concerts may be sold out.

So don't be disappointed. Send in your booking form today.

Concerts and booking information

The Concerts

Explaining our symbols

To simplify booking, the following symbols have been used above each concert listing:

 Each concert in the Proms season has its own performance number. This helps avoid confusion when there is more than one concert on a particular date.

 Denotes time the concert starts. Most, but not all, concerts begin at 7.30pm

 Denotes the Price Code for that particular concert.
Please note that if you wish to book any concerts from Price Codes B or C, priority will be given to your postal application if you have also chosen at least one concert from Price Code A.

 Denotes a concert with a premiere where a special discount applies. Please see page 113.

 'All-In' Tickets allow a discount on some afternoon and late-night concerts provided purchase is combined with the main evening concert. See page 117.

For Pre-Prom Talks and Lectures, see also page 124.

For Chamber Concerts see page 125.

Friday 19 July
7.30pm – c 9.40pm

Haydn
The Creation (in German)

Part I   34'

I N T E R V A L

Parts 2 and 3   60'

Juliane Banse soprano
Hans Peter Blochwitz tenor
Wolfgang Schöne baritone

BBC Symphony Chorus
BBC Symphony Orchestra
Andrew Davis conductor

The second century of the BBC Proms begins at the beginning. Never before performed on the First Night of the season, Haydn's life-enhancing celebration of the creation of the world from chaos (see also Proms 25, 29 and 35) praises humanity as God's greatest creation. It surveys the whole of created life: light, the natural world, animals, and finally man and woman, in a wealth of descriptive and powerful music.

Commentary by Nicholas Kenyon and Stephen Maddock

Saturday 20 July
6.00pm – c10.30pm

Verdi
Don Carlos
(five-act version, in Italian)

Acts 1 and 2	95'

I N T E R V A L

Act 3	40'

I N T E R V A L

Acts 4 and 5	80'

Elisabeth	**Galina Gorchakova** soprano
Princess Eboli	**Olga Borodina**
	mezzo-soprano
Don Carlos	**Richard Margison** tenor
Rodrigo	**Dmitri Hvorostovsky** baritone
King Philip II	**Roberto Scandiuzzi** bass
Grand Inquisitor	**Robert Lloyd** bass
Lerma	**Robin Leggate** tenor
Voice from Heaven	**Mary Plazas** soprano

Royal Opera Chorus
Orchestra of the Royal Opera House
Bernard Haitink conductor

In collaboration with the Royal Opera's Verdi Festival, the Proms present an outstanding cast in one of the greatest Verdi operas, in a version different from that recently staged at Covent Garden.

Pre-Prom Talk at 4.45pm
Charles Osborne

Sunday 21 July
7.30pm – c9.50pm

Weill
The Silver Lake *(in German)*

Act 1	55'

I N T E R V A L

Acts 2 and 3	55'

Fennimore	**Juanita Lascarro** soprano
Frau von Luber	**Helga Dernesch**
	mezzo-soprano
Baron Laur	**Heinz Zednik** tenor
Severin	**Heinz Kruse** tenor
Lottery Agent	**Graham Clark** tenor
1st Shopgirl	**Catrin Wyn-Davies** soprano
2nd Shopgirl	**Katarina Karnéus**
	mezzo-soprano
Gravedigger	**Gidon Saks** bass-baritone

London Sinfonietta Chorus
London Sinfonietta
Markus Stenz conductor

Kurt Weill's last work written for Germany, before he left the country in 1933, is one of the sharpest reflections of that turbulent era. The music is gritty, jazz-influenced: David Drew describes 'one of Weill's finest scores' on page 46.

Pre-Prom Talk at 6.15pm
David Drew

Monday 22 July
7.30pm – c9.45pm

Chabrier orch. Robin Holloway	
Bourrée fantasque	5'
Roussel	
Bacchus et Ariane	37'

I N T E R V A L

Dominic Muldowney	
Trombone Concerto	c20'
BBC commission: world premiere	
Musorgsky orch. Ravel	
Pictures at an Exhibition	33'

Christian Lindberg trombone

BBC Philharmonic
Yan Pascal Tortelier conductor

Ravel's spectacular scoring of Musorgsky's *Pictures* and Robin Holloway's homage to Chabrier open a series of pieces in which composers reimagine earlier music (see page 6). The extrovert trombonist Christian Lindberg plays this season's first new commission, which pays homage to the comic Tony Hancock.

Chamber Music at 1.00pm
Pre-Prom Talk at 6.15pm
Dominic Muldowney

Tuesday 23 July
7.30pm – c9.40pm

Bach orch. Elgar	
Fantasia and Fugue in C minor	9'
Hans Werner Henze	
Three Pieces for Orchestra	
UK premiere	c15'
Rakhmaninov	
Rhapsody on a Theme of Paganini	22'

I N T E R V A L

Brahms	
Symphony No. 4 in E minor	42'

Nikolai Lugansky piano

BBC Philharmonic
Vassily Sinaisky conductor

The BBC Philharmonic's new Principal Guest Conductor introduces to this country the seventy-year-old Hans Werner Henze's homage to Karl Amadeus Hartmann. More reworkings of old music are heard in Rakhmaninov's virtuoso transformation of Paganini, Elgar's colourful version of a Bach organ work, and Brahms's Fourth, whose chaconne pays homage to Bach.

BBC Philharmonic Workshop at 11.00am
Pre-Prom Talk at 6.15pm
Hans Werner Henze

6 | £A

Wednesday 24 July
7.30pm – c9.35pm

Wagner
Overture and Venusberg Music
from 'Tannhäuser'   24'

Strauss
Four Last Songs   21'

I N T E R V A L

Dvořák
In Nature's Realm   15'

Bax
Spring Fire   30'

Christine Brewer soprano

BBC Symphony Orchestra
Mark Elder conductor

Bax's atmospheric picture of nature
and creation is one of the finest British
works from early this century, never
before heard at the Proms. Contrasting
sounds of nature are evoked by Dvořák
and Wagner, while Richard Strauss's
songs capture a mood of regretful
farewell, and are sung by the
outstanding soprano from last Prom
season's *War Requiem*.

7 | £A

Thursday 25 July
7.00pm – c9.15pm

Berthold Goldschmidt
Passacaglia, Op. 4   7'
first UK concert performance

Mendelssohn
Violin Concerto in E minor   26'

I N T E R V A L

Shostakovich
Symphony No. 11
'The Year 1905'   63'

Christian Tetzlaff violin

Bournemouth Symphony Orchestra
Yakov Kreizberg conductor

The dynamic new partnership of
Yakov Kreizberg and the
Bournemouth Symphony Orchestra
continues the remarkable revival of
interest in the music of Berthold
Goldschmidt with an early prize-
winning work from 1926.
Mendelssohn's popular, lyrical concerto
leads to the massive Eleventh
Symphony of Shostakovich, which
although describing the events of the
1905 Revolution was written in the
shadow of the Soviet invasion of
Hungary in 1956.

Pre-Prom Talk at 5.45pm
Berthold Goldschmidt

8 | £D

Thursday 25 July
10.00pm – c11.20pm

'Dawn at Dusk'
American operatic arias and popular
song by Bernstein, Carlisle Floyd, Weill,
Rodgers and Hart, Gershwin, Blitzstein,
and Sondheim

Dawn Upshaw soprano

Fred Hersch piano

London Sinfonietta
Eric Stern conductor

Dawn Upshaw reached a huge
audience through her recording of
Górecki's Third Symphony: she is one
of the most versatile and talented of a
new generation of American singers.
In a specially devised late-night recital,
she ranges from American opera to
show songs by Bernstein, Weill and
Stephen Sondheim (whose music is
heard for the first time at a Prom).

9 | £A

Friday 26 July
7.30pm – c9.35pm

Lutoslawski
Novelette   17'

Britten
Four Sea-Interludes and Passacaglia
from 'Peter Grimes'   24'

I N T E R V A L

Shostakovich
Symphony No. 5 in D minor   44'

London Symphony Orchestra
Mstislav Rostropovich conductor

Three masterpieces by three composers
who were all close friends of tonight's
conductor. Rostropovich this year
conducted the first performances in
Vienna of Britten's *Peter Grimes*; he
gave the premiere of Lutoslawski's
Novelette when he was conductor of
the National Symphony in
Washington. Shostakovich was a
lifelong colleague whose Fifth
Symphony is among this century's
most powerful masterworks; the
ninetieth anniversary of his birth is
celebrated this year.

Saturday 27 July
7.30pm – c 9.50pm

Mozart
Symphony No. 35 in D major
'Haffner'   20'

Piano Concerto No. 19
in F major, K459   27'

I N T E R V A L

Brahms
Variations on the
St Anthony Chorale   17'

Mozart
Piano Concerto No. 22
in E flat major, K482   34'

András Schiff piano

English Chamber Orchestra
George Malcolm conductor

One of the central figures in British musical life as choirmaster, harpsichordist, accompanist and conductor, George Malcolm approaches his eightieth birthday and collaborates with his friend and pupil András Schiff, now one of the world's leading pianists, in a sunny programme including one of Mozart's most extrovert symphonies and two of his finest piano concertos.

Sunday 28 July
7.30pm – c 9.40pm

Falla
Atlántida – suite   36'
London premiere

Ravel
Piano Concerto for the Left Hand   18'

I N T E R V A L

Beethoven
Symphony No. 7 in A major   38'

María Bayo soprano
Katarina Karnéus mezzo-soprano
William Dazeley baritone

Louis Lortie piano

BBC Singers
BBC Symphony Chorus
BBC Symphony Orchestra
Rafael Frühbeck de Burgos conductor

The Spanish composer Manuel de Falla died fifty years ago, leaving a great project unfinished: an oratorio about the discovery of Atlantis, as told to Columbus. Rafael Frühbeck de Burgos has selected extracts to be heard for the first time in London, alongside music by Ravel, who influenced Falla, and Beethoven's eternally fresh 'apotheosis of the dance'.

BBC SO workshop at 6.00pm

Monday 29 July
7.30pm – c 9.45pm

Mozart
Symphony No. 23
in D major, K181   9'

Haydn
Mass in Time of War
(Paukenmesse)   40'

I N T E R V A L

Haydn
The Storm   10'

Mozart
Symphony No. 41 in C major
'Jupiter'   33'

Susan Gritton soprano
Catherine Wyn-Rogers
mezzo-soprano
Ian Bostridge tenor
Gerald Finley baritone

Choir of The English Concert
The English Concert
Trevor Pinnock conductor

Trevor Pinnock's exuberant performances of Haydn and Mozart are well known through his recordings: here he couples one of Haydn's great late Masses and two Mozart symphonies with Haydn's programmatic 'madrigal', related to *The Creation*.

Chamber Music at 1.00pm

Tuesday 30 July
7.30pm – c 9.35pm

Wagner
The Mastersingers of Nuremberg –
suite   19'

Schoenberg
Chamber Symphony No. 1
(orchestral version)   22'

I N T E R V A L

Brahms
Piano Concerto No. 2
in B flat major   49'

Stephen Hough piano

BBC National Orchestra of Wales
Mark Wigglesworth conductor

Mark Wigglesworth gives his first Prom as Music Director of the BBC National Orchestra of Wales, presenting Schoenberg's epoch-making First Chamber Symphony in a version the composer made for full orchestra, alongside one of the greatest nineteenth-century concertos by Brahms, whose music Schoenberg so much admired, and extracts from Wagner's sublime comic opera.

Wednesday 31 July
7.30pm – c9.55pm

John Pickard
The Flight of Icarus   20'
London premiere

Shostakovich
Cello Concerto No. 1   27'

I N T E R V A L

Rakhmaninov
Symphony No. 2 in E minor   62'

Steven Isserlis cello

BBC National Orchestra of Wales
Mark Wigglesworth conductor

Russia dominates the BBC National
Orchestra of Wales's second
programme, with Rakhmaninov's vast
symphony and Shostakovich's sharp-
edged cello concerto, played by the
soloist who gave the premiere of
Tavener's *The Protecting Veil*. It is
prefaced by the first London
performance of one of the most
successful premieres the orchestra has
given in recent years: Gavin Thomas
writes about this piece of 'whirlwind
orchestral virtuosity' on page 72.

Pre-Prom Talk at 6.15pm
John Pickard

Thursday 1 August
7.30pm – c9.50pm

Bruckner
Symphony No. 2 in C minor   64'

I N T E R V A L

Stravinsky
Capriccio for Piano and Orchestra 17'

Alfred Schnittke
arr. Gennady Rozhdestvensky
Dead Souls – suite   20'
London premiere

Victoria Postnikova piano

BBC Symphony Orchestra
Gennady Rozhdestvensky conductor

Opening the Proms celebration of
Bruckner's centenary is his rarely-heard
Second Symphony, an expansive and
lyrical work; Andrew Huth explores
Bruckner's insecure genius on page 24.
Rozhdestvensky, returning to the
orchestra of which he was Chief
Conductor, introduces to London a
colourful and quirky suite he has
drawn from film music by Alfred
Schnittke, and is joined by his wife
Victoria Postnikova in the piano
concerto Stravinsky wrote for himself
to play.

Friday 2 August
7.00pm – c9.05pm

Bach
Suite No. 3 in D major   19'

Handel
Julius Caesar – excerpts   40'

I N T E R V A L

Bach
Magnificat   28'

María Bayo soprano
Susan Gritton soprano
Andreas Scholl counter-tenor
Jamie MacDougall tenor
Peter Kooy bass

Choir of New College, Oxford
Choir of Winchester Cathedral
**Orchestra of the Age of
Enlightenment**
René Jacobs conductor

Baroque music of brilliance and
confidence: Bach's *Magnificat* is his
most taut and concise choral work,
while his Suite No. 3 includes the
so-called 'Air on the G string'.
Handel's operas, finally winning the
recognition they deserve, are crowded
with expressive and thrilling music.
René Jacobs, after a long career as a
counter-tenor, is now a leading
early-music director and makes his
Proms debut.

Friday 2 August
10.00pm – c12.00 midnight

Indian music
Calcutta Drum Orchestra   40'

Pandit Shivkumar Sharma santoor
Pandit Anindo Chatterjee tabla   60'

Created and led by the great tabla
maestro Pandit Shankar Ghosh, the
Calcutta Drum Orchestra is a unique
group of musicians who perform on
various North Indian drums, giving a
totally new dimension to the already
intricate concepts of North Indian
rhythm. Shivkumar Sharma is a
technically brilliant and creatively
unique musician, a virtuoso of the
North Indian santoor. He is
accompanied by the superlative tabla
playing of Anindo Chatterjee.

Saturday 3 August
7.30pm – c 9.40pm

Strauss
Don Juan 17'

Elgar
Enigma Variations 32'

I N T E R V A L

Sibelius
Symphony No. 2 in D major 42'

European Union Youth Orchestra
Sir Colin Davis conductor

Three surefire orchestral showpieces for talented young players drawn from around Europe. Strauss's portrait of a hero has been described as 'a one-movement opera without voices', a dramatic piece of story-telling which leads to Elgar's portraits of friends and colleagues, each deftly drawn and sharply characterised. Sir Colin Davis has been acclaimed for his recent Sibelius symphony performances.

Sunday 4 August
4.00pm – c5.40pm

'Spirituals of Struggle' 12'

Randall Thompson
The Peaceable Kingdom – excerpts 13'

'Spirituals of Struggle' 10'

I N T E R V A L

Shelton E. Kilby III
Who Has Set Thy Glory 13'
world premiere

'Spirituals of Freedom' 20'

London Adventist Chorale
Ken Burton conductor

The London Adventist Chorale was the winner of the Sainsbury's Choir of the Year competition last year: their superbly drilled yet spontaneous gospel singing won all hearts. The commitment and religious fervour of their performances are matched by their warmth and precision. They come to the Proms in a mixed programme of spirituals and sacred songs, plus the first performance of a work they commissioned, made possible by Sainsbury's as part of their prize.

Sunday 4 August
7.30pm – c 9.40pm

Ives orch. Schuman
Variations on 'America' 7'

Ives arr. Gunther Schuller
The General Slocum 3'

The Yale–Princeton
Football Game 3'

Copland
Organ Symphony 25'

I N T E R V A L

John Adams
Violin Concerto 30'

Duke Ellington
Harlem 15'

Simon Preston organ
Ernst Kovacic violin

BBC Symphony Orchestra
Leonard Slatkin conductor

Returning to the Proms, Leonard Slatkin provides a panorama across this century's pioneering American music, including the prize-winning Violin Concerto by John Adams and a work by Duke Ellington, whose music is being heard for the first time at a Prom.

Pre-Prom Talk at 6.15pm
Leonard Slatkin

Monday 5 August
6.30pm – c10.05pm

Handel
Semele

Act 1 55'

I N T E R V A L

Act 2 40'

I N T E R V A L

Act 3 65'

Semele — Rosemary Joshua soprano
Cadmus — Reinhard Hagen bass
Ino — Charlotte Hellekant mezzo-soprano
Athamas — Michael Chance counter-tenor
Jupiter — Paul Groves tenor
Juno — Kathleen Kuhlmann mezzo-soprano
Iris — Sophie Marin-Degor soprano
Somnus — Willard White bass

Les Arts Florissants
William Christie conductor

'Endless pleasure, endless love': Semele's show-stopping aria is the best-known number from one of Handel's richest and most dramatic scores. William Christie conducts Handel at Glyndebourne this year: here he brings his own world-renowned ensemble to make a first appearance in the Albert Hall.

Chamber Music at 1.00pm

Tuesday 6 August
7.30pm – c9.35pm

Nielsen
Overture 'Helios' — 10'

Sir Peter Maxwell Davies
Symphony No. 6 — c40'
London premiere

I N T E R V A L

Sibelius
Violin Concerto — 32'

Lemminkäinen's Return — 6'

Tasmin Little violin

Royal Philharmonic Orchestra
Sir Peter Maxwell Davies conductor

One of the most successful recent Prom premieres was Sir Peter Maxwell Davies's Fifth Symphony; here is its successor in its first hearing in London. His links to the Northern lands are explored further in music by Nielsen and Sibelius, with the Violin Concerto played by the popular soloist from the 1995 Last Night.

Pre-Prom Talk at 6.15pm
Sir Peter Maxwell Davies

Wednesday 7 August
7.00pm – c10.00pm

MacCunn
The Ship o' the Fiend — 12'

Schumann
Piano Concerto in A minor — 31'

I N T E R V A L

Tan Dun
On Taoism* — 14'
London premiere

Orchestral Theatre II: Re* — 22'
London premiere

I N T E R V A L

Walton
Symphony No. 2 — 28'

Lars Vogt piano

Stephen Richardson bass

BBC Scottish Symphony Orchestra
Martyn Brabbins conductor
Tan Dun conductor *

An evergreen of the Romantic repertory and a striking work by Walton frame music by the Chinese-American composer Tan Dun, who draws his inspiration from natural sounds. Be prepared to join in!

Pre-Prom Talk at 5.45pm
Tan Dun

Thursday 8 August
7.00pm – c9.15pm

Lyadov
Baba-Yaga — 3'
The Enchanted Lake — 8'
Kikimora — 7'

Mozart
Clarinet Concerto in A major — 28'

I N T E R V A L

Shostakovich
Symphony No. 10 in E minor — 52'

Michael Collins clarinet

Russian National Orchestra
Mikhail Pletnev conductor

The Proms welcome for the first time the virtuoso Russian orchestra created by pianist and conductor Mikhail Pletnev. Lyadov's atmospheric poems are rarely played together, and Shostakovich's Tenth – written soon after the death of Stalin – is one of the most accessible and powerful of postwar symphonies. Michael Collins plays Mozart's concerto on the richly-toned basset clarinet for which it was intended.

Thursday 8 August
10.00pm – c11.20pm

Rameau
Overture 'Zaïs' — 6'

Motet 'In convertendo' — 24'

Rebel
'Chaos' from 'The Elements' — 7'

Charpentier
Te Deum — 24'

Claron McFadden soprano
Guillemette Laurens soprano
Simon Berridge haute-contre
Rodrigo del Pozo haute-contre
Andrew King tenor
Nicolas Robertson tenor
Nicolas Cavallier bass
Nicolas Rivenq bass

St James's Singers
St James's Baroque Players
Ivor Bolton conductor

Rebel's *The Elements* depicts chaos with an astonishing opening chord; the Overture to Rameau's *Zaïs* shows the whole of creation in the making (see Proms 1, 29 and 35). The rich tradition of French Baroque choral music reaches its height in Rameau's grand motets and the *Te Deum* by Charpentier (immortalised by Eurovision), which begins a Proms series of settings of this text.

26 £A

 **27** £A

 **28** £D
Stravinsky Day

 **29** £A
Stravinsky Day

26

Friday 9 August
7.30pm – c 9.50pm

Haydn
Symphony No. 94 in G major
'Surprise' 24'

Alfred Schnittke
Viola Concerto 33'

I N T E R V A L

Prokofiev
Symphony No. 7 43'

Yuri Bashmet viola

Russian National Orchestra
Mikhail Pletnev conductor

Schnittke's intense Viola Concerto has quickly established itself as a modern classic: it is here played by the virtuoso to whom it is dedicated. Pletnev has had great success in Haydn, as pianist and conductor; the companion symphony, Prokofiev's Seventh, is among his most genial and likeable works, light in tone but strong in substance.

27

Saturday 10 August
7.30pm – c 9.45pm

Varèse
Amériques 23'

Gershwin
But not for me
How long has this been going on?
Slap that bass
Someone to watch over me
The Lorelei 15'

An American in Paris 18'

I N T E R V A L

Stravinsky
The Rite of Spring 33'

Sally Burgess mezzo-soprano

National Youth Orchestra of Great Britain
Paul Daniel conductor

The National Youth Orchestra Prom is always a highlight of the season, and this ingenious programme, conducted by the newly announced Music Director of English National Opera, juxtaposes Stravinsky's primal ballet, first seen in Paris, with Gershwin's fizzy response to that city and Varèse's massive sound-sculpture, a Proms premiere.

Inaugural BBC Proms Lecture at 4.00pm

28

Sunday 11 August
4.00pm – c 5.00pm

Stravinsky
The Soldier's Tale (semi-staged) 55'

Members of Birmingham Royal Ballet
Birmingham Contemporary Music Group
Oliver Hindle choreographer
Daniel Harding conductor

For the first time, the Proms devote three concerts on one day to a single composer, exploring the towering genius of Igor Stravinsky, who died a quarter of a century ago. Both his originality and his influence can be heard across the concerts, starting with the work that almost single-handedly created the genre of music-theatre. Dancers and musicians from Birmingham, performing in the Albert Hall arena, collaborate under Daniel Harding, who becomes the youngest-ever conductor at the Proms.

29

Sunday 11 August
6.30pm – c 8.35pm

Stravinsky
The Fairy's Kiss 43'

I N T E R V A L

Gesualdo arr. Stravinsky
Tres Sacrae Cantiones* 11'

Stravinsky
Monumentum pro Gesualdo
di Venosa ad CD annum 8'

The Flood 20'

Satan Robert Tear tenor
God/Noah's Sons
David Wilson-Johnson bass-baritone
Stephen Richardson bass
Narrator Simon Callow (tbc)

New London Chamber Choir
BBC Symphony Orchestra
Oliver Knussen conductor
James Wood conductor*

Stravinsky's The Flood, telling with wit and verve part of the creation story and framed by a setting of the Te Deum, links two themes of this year's Proms; The Fairy's Kiss, reimagining Tchaikovsky, and the reworkings of the fevered music of Gesualdo, show Stravinsky as a master of another Proms theme of creative recreation.

30 **£D**

Stravinsky Day

 **31** **£A**

 32 **£A** PREMIERE VOUCHER

     33 **£A**

Sunday 11 August
9.30pm – c10.45pm

Stravinsky
Cantata   23'

Concerto for Piano and Wind   19'

Mass   18'

Teresa Shaw mezzo-soprano
Neil Jenkins tenor

Wayne Marshall piano

Taverner Choir
Birmingham Contemporary Music
Group
Andrew Parrott conductor

The exquisite restraint of Stravinsky's
Mass setting and the vocal elaboration
of his Cantata (new to the Proms)
show how he reinvented the music of
the distant past with piercing
originality, and contrast with the
bubbling rhythmic energy of his
Concerto for Piano and Wind.
Andrew Parrott's skilled Taverner vocal
forces collaborate with Birmingham's
expert new music players.

Monday 12 August
7.30pm – c9.30pm

Gerhard
The Plague   45'

I N T E R V A L

Rodrigo
Concierto de Aranjuez   23'

Ravel
Bolero   15'

John Williams guitar

BBC Singers
BBC Symphony Chorus
Joven Orquesta Nacional de España
Edmon Colomer conductor

Rodrigo's ever-popular guitar
concerto, played by one of the greatest
guitarists of our time, and Ravel's still-
revolutionary orchestral showpiece,
introduce a new Spanish orchestra of
young players, *The Plague* is a chilling,
impressionistic setting for narrator,
choir and orchestra of Camus's famous
story *La Peste*, revived to celebrate the
centenary of Roberto Gerhard, the
Spanish composer who settled in
Cambridge (see also Proms 35 and 60).

Chamber Music at 1.00pm

Tuesday 13 August
7.30pm – c9.35pm

Stravinsky
Symphonies of Wind Instruments   9'

Oliver Knussen
Horn Concerto   12'
London premiere

Debussy
Nocturnes   22'

I N T E R V A L

Mozart
Horn Concerto No. 3
in E flat major, K447   15'

Sibelius
Symphony No. 7   22'

Barry Tuckwell horn

Philharmonia Orchestra
Esa-Pekka Salonen conductor

Esa-Pekka Salonen conducts
twentieth-century masterpieces,
including the London premiere of
Oliver Knussen's light and lyrical Horn
Concerto. Barry Tuckwell plays this,
and Mozart, in his farewell London
appearance as a horn player.

Pre-Prom Talk at 6.15pm
Oliver Knussen

Wednesday 14 August
7.30pm – c9.40pm

Vaughan Williams
Fantasia on a Theme
by Thomas Tallis   15'

John Woolrich
Oboe Concerto   c20'
BBC commission: world premiere

Bach orch. Stokowski
Passacaglia and Fugue in C minor   12'

I N T E R V A L

Brahms orch. Schoenberg
Piano Quartet No. 1 in G minor   45'

Nicholas Daniel oboe

BBC Symphony Orchestra
Matthias Bamert conductor

Vaughan Williams's debt to Tudor
music and Schoenberg's devotion to
Brahms were central to their creative
lives. The multicoloured arrangement
of Bach by Stokowski contrasts with
the riotous excesses of Schoenberg's
Brahms orchestration. Nick Kimberley
introduces John Woolrich's new work
on page 58.

BBC SO project and talk at 6.00pm
John Woolrich

34 £A	**35** £D	**36** £B	**37** £A

Thursday 15 August
7.00pm – c 9.05pm

Janáček
Schluck und Jau – incidental music   9'

Liszt
Piano Concerto No. 1
in E flat major   19'

I N T E R V A L

Berlioz
Symphonie fantastique   55'

Artur Pizarro piano

**Royal Liverpool Philharmonic
Orchestra
Libor Pešek** conductor

The acclaimed Portuguese pianist
Artur Pizarro returns for his fourth
Proms appearance in a heady piece of
musical Romanticism, preceded by a
Janáček rarity which is a Libor Pešek
speciality. Berlioz's high-tension,
fevered *Symphonie fantastique* will
provide an opportunity to hear the
successful collaboration between Pešek
and his Liverpool orchestra at full
stretch.

Thursday 15 August
10.00pm – c11.25pm

Milhaud
La Création du monde   16'

Falla
Psyché   5'

Colin Matthews
Twenty-Three Frames for Four Players
    13'

Gerhard arr. Meirion Bowen
Six Songs from 'L'infantament
meravellos de Shahrazada'   16'

Falla
El corregidor y la molinéra – Act 1   15'

Rosa Mannion soprano

**Nash Ensemble
Martyn Brabbins** conductor

The conjunction of the Gerhard and
Falla anniversaries provides a chance to
compare their contributions to the
adventurousness of Spanish music this
century. Their scores, shot through
with the hard, bright lyricism of the
Iberian peninsula, are here joined by a
recent Nash commission, as Colin
Matthews reaches fifty, and Milhaud's
jazz-inspired portrait of creation (see
Proms 1, 25 and 29).

Friday 16 August
7.00pm – c 9.50pm

Beethoven
Leonore (*semi-staged*)

Acts 1 and 2   85'

I N T E R V A L

Act 3   54'

Leonore   **Charlotte Margiono** soprano
Florestan   **Kim Begley** tenor
Don Pizarro   **Matthew Best** bass
Rocco   **Franz Hawlata** bass
Marzelline   **Christiane Oelze** soprano
Jaquino   **Michael Schade** tenor
Don Fernando   **Geert Smits** baritone

**Monteverdi Choir
Orchestre Révolutionnaire et
Romantique
John Eliot Gardiner** conductor

Fresh from their exploration of
Beethoven's symphonies, John Eliot
Gardiner and his period-instrument
players now look towards his operatic
output, and the music that led towards
his masterpiece *Fidelio*. David Cairns,
who introduces Beethoven's *Leonore* on
page 42, describes it as 'magnificent
music ... it demands to be heard'.

Saturday 17 August
7.30pm – c 9.50pm

Dvořák
Te Deum   20'

Mozart
Piano Concerto No. 27
in B flat major, K595   30'

I N T E R V A L

Martinů
Field Mass   20'

Janáček
Sinfonietta   24'

Judith Howarth soprano
Ivan Kusnjer baritone

Richard Goode piano

**BBC Symphony Chorus
BBC Symphony Orchestra
Jiří Bělohlávek** conductor

The BBC Symphony Orchestra's new
Principal Guest Conductor gives his
first Prom with them, ending with
Janáček's blazing Sinfonietta and
beginning with Dvořák's response to
the timeless words of the *Te Deum* (see
Proms 25, 42 and 72), which was
premiered in America in honour of
Columbus (see Prom 11).

38 £B

39 £B

40 £B

41 £C

Sunday 18 August
7.30pm – c9.45pm

Rossini
Overture
'The Italian Girl in Algiers'　　8'

Grieg
Solveig's Song
Solveig's Lullaby
From Monte Pincio
A Swan
Spring　　20'

I N T E R V A L

Mahler
Symphony No. 5　　71'

Barbara Bonney soprano

Oslo Philharmonic Orchestra
Mariss Jansons conductor

Mariss Jansons has raised the Oslo Philharmonic to world stature, and their Proms visits have been favourite occasions for nearly a decade. Norwegian music features in the songs by Grieg sung by American soprano Barbara Bonney, while the evening's symphony is Mahler's five-movement journey from darkness to light, with its famous Adagietto.

Monday 19 August
7.30pm – c9.40pm

Bartók
Music for Strings,
Percussion and Celesta　　30'

I N T E R V A L

Alfred Janson
Interlude for Orchestra　　11'
UK premiere

Dvořák
Symphony No. 9 in E minor
'From the New World'　　45'

Oslo Philharmonic Orchestra
Mariss Jansons conductor

Dvořák's last symphony, first performed in 1893, is one of the most popular of all orchestral works, and Mariss Jansons has made a speciality of his music. It draws on folk music traditions, as in a very different style does Bartók's eerie, taut masterpiece: its unique sound depends on a divided orchestra and the percussive sounds of piano and celesta. Born in 1937, the pianist and composer Alfred Janson has a mixed jazz and classical background; his 1985 Interlude is a regular item in the Oslo orchestra's repertory.

Tuesday 20 August
7.30pm – c9.35pm

Strauss
Till Eulenspiegel　　15'

Ned Rorem
Cor Anglais Concerto　　22'
London premiere

I N T E R V A L

Tchaikovsky
Symphony No. 5 in E minor　　48'

Thomas Stacy cor anglais

New York Philharmonic
Kurt Masur conductor

Kurt Masur, who has been a regular Proms visitor, returns for the first time with the New York Philharmonic, of which he is now Music Director. Their triumphant partnership has resulted in many recordings and tours: for this visit they introduce here a lyrical concerto by an American composer best known for his vocal music, and bring two major orchestral showpieces.

Wednesday 21 August
7.30pm – c9.30pm

Brahms
Violin Concerto in D major　　40'

I N T E R V A L

Prokofiev
Romeo and Juliet – suite　　40'

Anne-Sophie Mutter violin

New York Philharmonic
Kurt Masur conductor

Anne-Sophie Mutter is a rare example of a child prodigy who has become an outstanding mature artist; she is now one of the most sought-after violinists in the world. She partners the New York Philharmonic in one of the peaks of the concerto repertory, and the orchestra offers a selection from one of the most sensational and colourful ballet scores written this century.

Chamber Music at 1.00pm

42 £A	**43** £D	**44** £A	**45** £A

Thursday 22 August
7.00pm – c 9.15pm

Wagner
Prelude and Liebestod
from 'Tristan and Isolde'   17'

Siegfried Matthus
Der Wald   18'
UK premiere

I N T E R V A L

Beethoven
Piano Concerto No. 3
in C minor   33'

Bruckner
Te Deum   23'

Andreas Haefliger piano

Yvonne Kenny soprano
Catherine Wyn-Rogers
mezzo-soprano
Thomas Randle tenor
Peter Sidhom baritone

Philharmonia Chorus
BBC Symphony Orchestra
Claus Peter Flor conductor

Three periods of German music come
together as Claus Peter Flor conducts
the BBC Symphony Orchestra for the
first time, including Bruckner's
triumphant *Te Deum* (see Proms 25, 37
and 72), and the first hearing in this
country of Matthus's timpani-
dominated tone-poem.

Thursday 22 August
10.00pm – c11.25pm

Messiaen
Oiseaux exotiques   14'

Mozart
Serenade in C minor, K388   22'

Stravinsky
Octet   15'

Kevin Volans
Piano Concerto   20'
BBC commission: UK premiere

Peter Donohoe piano

Netherlands Wind Ensemble
Daniel Harding conductor

A late-evening concert of wind-based
music from a distinguished ensemble
which draws on the best Dutch wind
players. The South African composer
Kevin Volans's highly original Piano
Concerto is introduced by Nick
Kimberley on page 58, and the concert
also includes one of Messiaen's
wonderful bird pieces, Stravinsky's
crisp octet and Mozart's dark-hued
'Nacht Musique'.

Friday 23 August
6.30pm – c10.20pm

Berg
Lulu (*semi-staged*)

Act 1   60'

I N T E R V A L

Act 2   55'

I N T E R V A L

Act 3   55'

Glyndebourne Festival Opera

Lulu   Christine Schäfer soprano
Geschwitz
          Kathryn Harries mezzo-soprano
Alwa   David Kuebler tenor
Dr Schön/Jack the Ripper
          Wolfgang Schöne baritone
Schigolch   Norman Bailey bass
and
Patricia Bardon mezzo-soprano
Donald Maxwell baritone
Stephan Drakulich tenor
Neil Jenkins tenor
Jonathan Veira baritone

The London Philharmonic
Andrew Davis conductor

Andrew Davis brings *Lulu* from
Glyndebourne to the Proms. Philip
Hensher writes on the work's
'voluptuousness' and 'sense of the
sublime' on page 48.

Saturday 24 August
7.30pm – c9.35pm

Smetana
Overture and Dance of the Comedians
from 'The Bartered Bride'   11'

'How strange and dead' from
'The Bartered Bride'   6'

Dvořák
'O Silver Moon' from 'Rusalka'   5'
Five Slavonic Dances   18'

I N T E R V A L

Johann Strauss II
Emperor Waltz   10'
Auf der Jagd – polka   2'
'Laughing Song' from
'Die Fledermaus'   4'

Lehár
'Vilja' from 'The Merry Widow'   5'

Johann Strauss II
Roses from the South   9'

Lumbye
Champagne Galop   2'

Johann Strauss II
Annen Polka   3'
By the Beautiful Blue Danube   9'

Rebecca Evans soprano

BBC Concert Orchestra
Barry Wordsworth conductor

46 £A

Sunday 25 August
7.30pm – c 9.40pm

Nielsen
Overture 'Maskarade'　　6'

Detlev Glanert
Symphony No. 3　　c20'
BBC commission: world premiere

Elgar
Cello Concerto in E minor　　30'

I N T E R V A L

Beethoven
Symphony No. 5 in C minor　　35'

Truls Mørk cello

BBC Scottish Symphony Orchestra
Osmo Vänskä conductor

Osmo Vänskä, who made his much-praised Proms debut last summer, has now been appointed Chief Conductor of the BBC Scottish Symphony Orchestra. He brings one of the most famous of all symphonies and one of the best-loved concertos (played by a new star among Scandinavian musicians), and premieres the 'symphony about old symphonies' by Detlev Glanert, introduced by Gavin Thomas on page 72.

Pre-Prom Talk at 6.15pm
Detlev Glanert

47 £A

Family Concert
Half price for under 14s
(not restricted view, Arena or Gallery)

Monday 26 August
11.30am – c 1.30pm

Walton
Overture 'Portsmouth Point'　　6'

Prokofiev
Lieutenant Kijé – suite　　19'

David Horne
Reaching Out　　10'

I N T E R V A L

Geoffrey Burgon
City Adventures
world premiere　　22'

Copland
Four Dance Episodes from 'Rodeo'　20'

Evelyn Glennie percussion

BBC Scottish Symphony Orchestra
Jerzy Maksymiuk conductor

A popular, approachable programme designed for family audiences of the 10+ age-range. The internationally famous percussionist Evelyn Glennie contrasts city and country in a dramatic solo work by David Horne inspired by Scottish landscapes, and a new orchestral showpiece written for her by *Brideshead Revisited* composer Geoffrey Burgon.

Chamber Music at 2.30pm

48 £A

Monday 26 August
7.00pm – c 9.45pm

Mendelssohn
Elijah (*in English*)
150th anniversary of first performance

Part 1　　65'

I N T E R V A L

Part 2　　65'

Bryn Terfel baritone
Janice Watson soprano
Susan Gritton soprano
Ingrid Attrot soprano
Jean Rigby mezzo-soprano
Pamela Helen Stephen mezzo-soprano
Anthony Rolfe Johnson tenor
Mark Tucker tenor
Christopher Purves baritone
Stephen Richardson bass

London Symphony Chorus
BBC National Chorus of Wales
BBC National Orchestra of Wales
Richard Hickox conductor

Mendelssohn's Biblical oratorio was first performed 150 years ago to the day, and quickly became one of the most popular of all choral works. Richard Hickox revives the score with outstanding Welsh baritone Bryn Terfel in the title-role, and the parts shared, as at the premiere, among ten singers.

49 £A

Tuesday 27 August
7.30pm – c 9.40pm

Beethoven
Symphony No. 8 in F major　　28'

György Kurtág
Stele
UK premiere　　13'

I N T E R V A L

Debussy
Prélude à l'après-midi d'un faune　10'

Ives
Symphony No. 4　　35'

BBC Singers
BBC Symphony Orchestra
Andrew Davis conductor

'A historic occasion', wrote the *Sunday Times* of Andrew Davis's performance of Ives's Fourth Symphony at the climax of the BBC Symphony Orchestra's Ives festival this January: a complex and chaotic vision for once precisely realised. The BBC Symphony Orchestra also brings a recent work by the Hungarian master György Kurtág to the Proms to mark his seventieth birthday, and adds two classic scores.

 **50** £C

   51 £C

 **52** £A

 **53** £D

Wednesday 28 August
7.30pm – c 9.45pm

Brahms
Piano Concerto No. 1
in D minor 47'

I N T E R V A L

Brahms
Symphony No. 1 in C minor 46'

Radu Lupu piano

Berlin Philharmonic Orchestra
Claudio Abbado conductor

Anticipating next year's Brahms
centenary, Claudio Abbado conducts
two of his finest works perfectly suited
to the strength and depth of the Berlin
Philharmonic's sound. Radu Lupu
made his Proms debut with this
concerto, and his many recordings and
performances have continued to
demonstrate his close affinity with
Brahms's music.

BBC SO Composers' Forum performance
at 6.00pm

Thursday 29 August
7.30pm – c 9.05pm

Mahler
Symphony No. 2 in C minor
'Resurrection' 85'

Solveig Kringelborn soprano
Marjana Lipovšek mezzo-soprano

BBC Symphony Chorus
London Symphony Chorus
Berlin Philharmonic Orchestra
Claudio Abbado conductor

The Berlin Philharmonic's last visit to
the Proms with Mahler's Ninth
Symphony under Claudio Abbado will
be remembered for ever by those who
were present. On this return visit they
bring Mahler's towering vision of
apocalypse and rebirth, joining forces
with London choruses for the vast
finale. See also page 80.

Friday 30 August
7.00pm – c 9.05pm

Elgar
Cockaigne 15'

Nicholas Maw
Violin Concerto 35'

I N T E R V A L

Vaughan Williams
Symphony No. 5 in D major 40'

Joshua Bell violin

The London Philharmonic
Roger Norrington conductor

An all-English programme from the
London Philharmonic and its Principal
Guest Conductor. It reflects Roger
Norrington's continuing exploration of
Vaughan Williams (with a symphony
premiered at the Proms in 1943) and
introduces one of the most successful
of recent violin concertos to the
Proms, a lyrical piece by Nicholas
Maw, played by the brilliant American
violinist who gave its premiere.

Pre-Prom Talk at 5.45pm
Nicholas Maw

10.00pm – c 11.25pm

Ives
From the Steeples and the
Mountains 3'

Set No. 1 for small orchestra 9'

György Kurtág
Samuel Beckett: What is the Word? 13'

Byrd
Ad Dominum cum tribularer* 11'

Carver
O bone Jesu* 11'

James Dillon
Oceanos c25'
BBC commission: world premiere

Ildikó Monyók reciter
Csaba Király piano

Polyphony
Music Projects/London
Richard Bernas conductor
Stephen Layton conductor*

György Kurtág and James Dillon
inhabit quite different worlds, but are
united by an uncompromising
integrity. Dillon's new *Oceanos* is the
last instalment of his major *Nine Rivers*
project, while Kurtág's enigmatic
setting of Samuel Beckett is unique.
The music of Renaissance Scots
composer Robert Carver has never
been heard at the Proms.

Saturday 31 August
7.30pm – c 9.45pm

Stravinsky
Pulcinella   40'

I N T E R V A L

Mark-Anthony Turnage
Your Rockaby   20'

Fauré
Requiem   36'

Joan Rodgers soprano
Bonaventura Bottone tenor
Alan Opie baritone

Martin Robertson saxophone

BBC Symphony Chorus
BBC Symphony Orchestra
Andrew Davis conductor

Stravinsky's witty and inventive
transformation of music he thought
was by Pergolesi is a supreme example
of creating a music for the present
from music of the past. Fauré's
austerely beautiful *Requiem* springs
from a distinctively French tradition.
The BBC Symphony Orchestra also
plays the atmospheric saxophone
concerto it commissioned from Mark-
Anthony Turnage.

Pre-Prom Talk at 6.15pm
Mark-Anthony Turnage

Sunday 1 September
2.30pm – c 4.45pm

Rameau
Les Fêtes d'Hébé – suite   30'

I N T E R V A L

Haydn
Symphony No. 103 in E flat major
'Drumroll'   26'

Beethoven
Violin Concerto in D major   44'

Thomas Zehetmair violin

Orchestra of the Eighteenth Century
Frans Brüggen conductor

A remarkable day, bringing together
two of the world's leading chamber
orchestras, begins with the Proms
debut of the group Frans Brüggen
founded in 1981 from Europe's best
period-instrument players. Brüggen's
love of colour and adventure in music
has meant that Rameau has been a
speciality, as have Haydn's mature
symphonies. Thomas Zehetmair is
equally at home on period and
modern instruments.

Sunday 1 September
7.30pm – c 9.40pm

Mozart
Symphony No. 38 in D major
'Prague'   35'

I N T E R V A L

Schubert
Symphony No. 9 'Great C major'   55'

Chamber Orchestra of Europe
Nikolaus Harnoncourt conductor

Nikolaus Harnoncourt, like Brüggen,
began his career as a performer and
director of early music, but increasingly
he brings the fruits of that approach to
modern instruments, nowhere more
effectively than with the brilliant
Chamber Orchestra of Europe. His
recordings with them of the complete
Beethoven symphonies have been
hailed as revelatory, and here they
traverse the Classical era from Mozart
to Schubert.

Monday 2 September
7.30pm – c 9.35pm

Messiaen
Chronochromie   23'

I N T E R V A L

Bruckner
Symphony No. 7 in E major   70'

City of Birmingham Symphony
Orchestra
Sir Simon Rattle conductor

Sir Simon Rattle is only forty-one, but
already celebrates twenty years at the
Proms this summer. For the first time
he and the CBSO bring a Bruckner
symphony – one of the peaks of his
output – whose slow movement pays
moving homage to Wagner. A typically
provocative coupling places alongside
this opulence Messiaen's sharply etched
exploration of 'the colours of time'.

Chamber Music at 1.00pm

58 £B

Tuesday 3 September
7.00pm – c9.15pm

Berlioz
Overture 'The Corsair'　8'

Beethoven
Piano Concerto No. 5
in E flat major 'Emperor'　39'

I N T E R V A L

Sir Michael Tippett
Fantasia Concertante on a Theme
of Corelli　18'

Haydn
Symphony No. 88 in G major　22'

Alfred Brendel piano

**City of Birmingham Symphony
Orchestra**
Sir Simon Rattle conductor

Alfred Brendel, celebrating his sixty-fifth birthday this year, has often collaborated with Rattle, but never before at the Proms. They give Beethoven's grandest piano concerto, and Rattle continues the theme of recreation with Tippett's gorgeously ruminative reflections on Corelli. Not many conductors end concerts with Haydn, but Rattle has always had a strong commitment to his music.

59 £D

Tuesday 3 September
10.00pm – c11.15pm

Victoria
Tenebrae Responsories for Maundy
Thursday　6'

Andrew Simpson
The Hollow Hills　13'

Victoria
Tenebrae Responsories for Good
Friday　7'

James MacMillan
Màiri　10'

Victoria
Tenebrae Responsories for Holy
Saturday　5'

Britten
Sacred and Profane　15'

BBC Singers
Stephen Cleobury conductor

The BBC Singers' first Prom with their new Principal Conductor interleaves extracts from Victoria's expressive *Tenebrae Responsories*, sung during Holy Week, with Britten's virtuoso setting of Medieval English texts and two of the Singers' commissions from their recent seventieth-birthday series, both of which catch a new strain of lyricism in British music.

60 £A

Wednesday 4 September
7.30pm – c9.35pm

Ravel
Rapsodie espagnole　16'

Falla
Nights in the Gardens of Spain　22'

I N T E R V A L

Gerhard
Cancionero de Pedrell　18'

Falla
The Three-Cornered Hat –
Suites Nos. 1 and 2　26'

Joaquín Achúcarro piano

Jill Gomez soprano

BBC Philharmonic
Yan Pascal Tortelier conductor

An evening of extrovert Spanish (and Spanish-influenced) music, well suited to the lively partnership of Yan Pascal Tortelier and the BBC Philharmonic: Falla's tangy evocations of his homeland are contrasted with Ravel's exotic view of Spain from France, while Roberto Gerhard's attractive song-cycle is based on Spanish folk songs collected by his teacher Pedrell.

61 £A

Thursday 5 September
7.30pm – c9.20pm

Haydn
Symphony No. 76 in E flat major　23'

I N T E R V A L

Bruckner
Symphony No. 6 in A major　55'

BBC Symphony Orchestra
Günter Wand conductor

No celebration of the Bruckner centenary would be complete without a contribution from veteran German conductor Günter Wand, whose performances with the BBC Symphony Orchestra have been a highlight of previous Proms seasons. Here he explores with them for the first time the rugged and energetic Sixth Symphony, adding a Haydn symphony never yet heard in the 101 seasons of the Proms.

62 £A 🕐

Friday 6 September
7.30pm – c9.40pm

Debussy
The Martyrdom of Saint Sebastian – excerpts   *10'*

Prokofiev
Piano Concerto No. 2 in G minor   *32'*

I N T E R V A L

Stravinsky
The Firebird   *45'*

Alexander Toradze piano

Rotterdam Philharmonic Orchestra
Valery Gergiev conductor

The long-delayed Proms debut of the charismatic conductor Valery Gergiev: he brings with him the orchestra of which he is now music director alongside his leadership of the Kirov Opera. Tonight's music was all composed within three fruitful years, in the heady period just before the First World War.

---

63 £A 🕐

Saturday 7 September
8.00pm – c10.05pm

Prokofiev
Symphony No. 6   *42'*

I N T E R V A L

Musorgsky orch. Edison Denisov
The Nursery   *15'*
UK premiere

Debussy
La Mer   *27'*

Anna Netrebko soprano

Rotterdam Philharmonic Orchestra
Valery Gergiev conductor

Prokofiev and Musorgsky are composers close to Valery Gergiev's heart, and he has often conducted their operas: Prokofiev's Sixth Symphony is a conflict-ridden work written half a century ago, while Musorgsky's delightful *The Nursery* is heard here in the orchestration by Russian composer Edison Denisov and sung by a rising star of the Kirov Opera, seen in BBC2's *Ruslan and Lyudmila*.

BBC SO workshop at 6.30pm

---

64 £A 🕐

Sunday 8 September
7.30pm – c9.40pm

Rimsky-Korsakov
Capriccio espagnol   *16'*

Falla
El amor brujo   *26'*

I N T E R V A L

Xavier Montsalvatge
Five Negro Songs   *14'*

Stravinsky
Petrushka   *34'*

Della Jones mezzo-soprano

BBC National Orchestra of Wales
David Atherton conductor

The colours and rhythms of Spain are to the fore in Falla's ballet, which includes the famous *Ritual Fire Dance*, and an entertaining song-cycle by Xavier Montsalvatge. Rimsky-Korsakov provided one of the most enduring pictures of Spain, even though he never visited the country, while *Petrushka* completes this season's traversal of Stravinsky's greatest ballet scores.

---

65 🕐

Junior Prom

Monday 9 September
2.30pm – c4.15pm

Around the World in Eighty Minutes

Tony Robinson presenter

New London Children's Choir
BBC Concert Orchestra
Ronald Corp conductor

A lightning musical tour takes us, like Jules Verne's traveller, around the globe from London and back, experiencing a huge variety of sights and sounds on the way. This innovatory Junior Prom is specially designed for children between six and fourteen.

See page 110 for special booking arrangements. For further information, please call 0171 765 5666 by 20 May.

Chamber Music at 1.00pm

66	67	68	69

Monday 9 September
7.30pm – c 9.50pm

Takemitsu
Star-Isle   7'

Rakhmaninov
Piano Concerto No. 3 in D minor   43'

I N T E R V A L

Anthony Powers
Symphony   30'
world premiere

Respighi
Pines of Rome   20'

Leif Ove Andsnes piano

BBC National Orchestra of Wales
Tadaaki Otaka conductor

A titanic challenge in the concerto repertory, Rakhmaninov's Third is played by a brilliant young Norwegian pianist. Anthony Powers has established a quietly atmospheric voice in new music; Gavin Thomas introduces his new Symphony on page 72, and the concert begins with a tribute to Tōru Takemitsu, who died in February.

Tuesday 10 September
7.00pm – c 9.05pm

Sir Michael Tippett
The Rose Lake   28'

Prokofiev
Violin Concerto No. 1 in D major 22'

I N T E R V A L

Sibelius
Symphony No. 5 in E flat major   30'

Sarah Chang violin

BBC Symphony Orchestra
Andrew Davis conductor

Youth and old age meet in this Prom: the fifteen-year-old violinist Sarah Chang, acclaimed internationally, plays Prokofiev, while the ninety-one-year-old Sir Michael Tippett has his wonderful evocation of a Senegal landscape, *The Rose Lake*, played for the first time at the Proms. It was premiered last year, and he has insisted that it is his last orchestral work. Andrew Davis, a long-time advocate of Tippett's music, complements it with one of Sibelius's most popular symphonies.

Tuesday 10 September
10.00pm – c 11.20pm

Bach
Cantata No. 105 'Herr, gehe
nicht ins Gericht'   22'

Motet 'Der Geist hilft unser
Schwachheit auf'   9'

Mass in G minor, BWV235   30'

Vasilka Jezovšek soprano
Andreas Scholl counter-tenor
James Taylor tenor
Peter Kooy bass

Chorus and Orchestra of Collegium
Vocale, Ghent
Philippe Herreweghe conductor

Philippe Herreweghe has played a central part in the revolutionary developments in Bach performance over recent decades, creating a new, gently inflected style with his highly skilled players and singers. He brings them to the Proms for the first time with one of Bach's endlessly inventive short Masses and an outstanding cantata.

Wednesday 11 September
7.30pm – c 9.40pm

Henri Dutilleux
Violin Concerto
'L'Arbre des songes'   22'

I N T E R V A L

Messiaen
Turangalîla Symphony   75'

Olivier Charlier violin

Jean-Yves Thibaudet piano
Valerie Hartmann-Claverie
ondes martenot

BBC Philharmonic
Yan Pascal Tortelier conductor

Messiaen's massive symphony celebrating the power of love is now firmly established as one of the classics of the postwar era and a Proms favourite. Here outstanding French soloists join Yan Pascal Tortelier; he celebrates the eightieth birthday of his friend and compatriot Henri Dutilleux with the first Proms performance of his ravishing Violin Concerto, 'The Tree of Dreams'.

Pre-Prom Talk at 6.15pm
Anthony Powers

Pre-Prom Talk at 5.45pm
Sir Michael Tippett and Meirion Bowen

The Last Night of the Proms

Thursday 12 September
7.30pm – c 9.40pm

Schoenberg
Five Pieces for Orchestra, Op. 16   18'

I N T E R V A L

Bruckner
Symphony No. 8 in C minor   77'

Chicago Symphony Orchestra
Daniel Barenboim conductor

Returning to the Proms for the first time under their Music Director Daniel Barenboim, the Chicago Symphony is one of the world's greatest orchestras, with a reputation ranging from major twentieth-century scores such as the Schoenberg pieces (which Henry Wood famously premiered at the Proms just after they were written) to the peaks of the Romantic repertory, among which Bruckner's Eighth brings to a fitting climax our celebration of the composer's centenary.

Friday 13 September
6.45pm – c 9.00pm

Bruckner
Prelude and Fugue in C minor
Locus iste
Os justi
Afferentur regi
Aequalis 1
Christus factus est
Aequalis 2
Ave Maria
Ecce sacerdos magnus   32'

John Scott organ
BBC Singers
Jane Glover conductor

I N T E R V A L

Beethoven
Symphony No. 9 in D minor
'Choral'   75'

Deborah Voigt soprano
Anne Sofie von Otter mezzo-soprano
Johan Botha tenor
René Pape bass

BBC Singers
London Voices
Chicago Symphony Orchestra
Sir Georg Solti conductor

Solti returns to the Proms for the 'Choral' Symphony on the penultimate night. Bruckner's glorious choral music precedes it, in the hall where the composer played the organ in 1871.

Saturday 14 September
7.30pm – c10.50pm

Haydn
Te Deum   10'

Poul Ruders
Concerto in Pieces   16'
BBC commission: London premiere

Mozart
'Deh vieni, non tardar' and
'Dove sono' from
'The Marriage of Figaro'
'Se viver non degg'io' from
'Mitridate, rè di Ponto'   16'

Shostakovich
Concerto for Piano,
Trumpet and Strings   18'

I N T E R V A L

Glinka
Overture 'Ruslan and Lyudmila'   5'

Sir Malcolm Arnold
The Sound Barrier   8'

Offenbach
Barcarolle from
'The Tales of Hoffmann'   4'

'Ah! j'aime les militaires' from
'The Grand Duchess of Gerolstein'   4'

Berlioz
'Le Spectre de la rose' from
'Les Nuits d'été'   6'

Puccini
Flower Duet from 'Madam Butterfly'   6'

Elgar
Pomp and Circumstance
March No. 1   5'

Henry Wood
Fantasia on British Sea-Songs   12'

Arne
Rule, Britannia!   5'

Parry orch. Elgar
Jerusalem   2'

Felicity Lott soprano
Ann Murray mezzo-soprano

Joanna MacGregor piano
John Wallace trumpet

BBC Singers
BBC Symphony Chorus
BBC Symphony Orchestra
Andrew Davis conductor

Gathering the strands of the season together, Haydn's magnificent setting of the *Te Deum* launches the final concert, and Poul Ruders's commission, a brilliant success at the BBC's 'Music Live 95' weekend, reworks Purcell to provide a new guide around the sounds of the orchestra. Two much-loved singers are the vocal soloists, and we also mark the seventy-fifth birthday of Sir Malcolm Arnold, before the traditional celebrations take their course.

Follow our five simple booking stages.

Select the concerts you wish to attend from the list on pages 86–104.

If you want to book tickets for the Last Night, please refer to the information on page 116.

For some days on which there is more than one concert, a special All-in Ticket rate applies. Please see page 117 for details.

Lunchtime chamber music recitals are held each Monday during the Proms season at the Royal College of Music. Please see page 125 for programme and booking details.

For details of Premiere Vouchers, see page 114.

Choose your concert

STAGE

2 Choose your seat

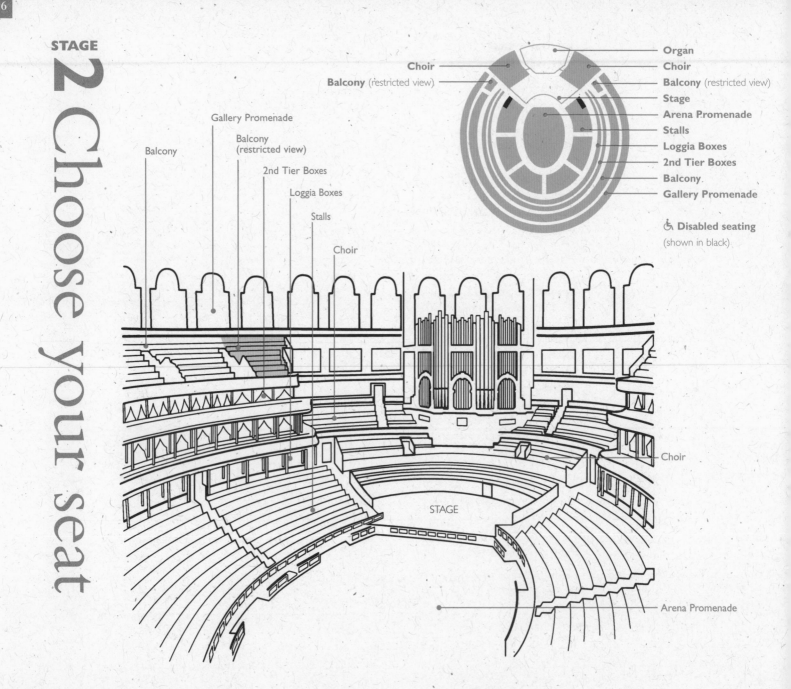

Organ

Choir

Choir

Balcony (restricted view)

Balcony (restricted view)

Stage

Arena Promenade

Stalls

Loggia Boxes

2nd Tier Boxes

Balcony

Gallery Promenade

♿ **Disabled seating**
(shown in black)

Balcony

Gallery Promenade

Balcony (restricted view)

2nd Tier Boxes

Loggia Boxes

Stalls

Choir

Choir

STAGE

Arena Promenade

Remember that each concert falls into one of five different price bands. Each band is colour coded for easy reference.

For Promenade tickets see page 115.

Last Night tickets see page 116.

● Premiere Vouchers see page 113.

↗ All-In Tickets see page 117.

Concert-goers with special needs see page 119.

Privately owned seats
A high proportion of boxes, as well as 600 stalls, are privately owned. Unless returned by owners, these seats are not available for sale.

Balcony
Prior to the 1996 Proms season, the Royal Albert Hall will complete an extensive refurbishment of the Balcony. New seating will offer increased leg-room, fewer restricted sightlines and a more comfortable environment.

A
Stalls £18.00
Loggia Boxes
(8 seats) and
2nd Tier Boxes
(5 seats) £14.50
Choir £12.50
Balcony £9.00
Balcony (restricted view) . . . £4.00

B
Stalls £23.00
Loggia Boxes
(8 seats) and
2nd Tier Boxes
(5 seats) £18.00
Choir £15.00
Balcony £10.00
Balcony (restricted view) . . . £4.00

C
Stalls £30.00
Loggia Boxes
(8 seats) and
2nd Tier Boxes
(5 seats) £25.00
Choir £18.00
Balcony £12.50
Balcony (restricted view) . . £5.00

D
Stalls £8.00
Loggia Boxes
(8 seats) and
2nd Tier Boxes
(5 seats) £8.00
Choir £8.00
Balcony £8.00
Balcony (restricted view) . . . N/A

E
Stalls £60.00
Loggia Boxes
(8 seats) and
2nd Tier Boxes
(5 seats) £60.00
Choir £40.00
Balcony £40.00
Balcony (restricted view) . . £18.00

STAGE 3 Choose your price bands

STAGE

4 Fill in the booking form

Fill in the number of tickets you require for each of your chosen concerts.

Be careful to write the number in the box under your chosen seating area.

Add up the amount spent on tickets at the end of each column (see example).

If the tickets you want are not available, lower-priced tickets for the same concert will be sent. Please tick the box on page 112 if this is NOT acceptable.

Tickets cannot be exchanged for other performances nor refunded except in the event of a cancelled performance. The BBC reserves the right to substitute artists and vary programmes if necessary.

Booking Queries

If you have any queries about how to fill in this booking form, please phone the box office on 0171 589 8212. But please note that telephone bookings cannot be made until 10 June.

Car Parking

£5.00 per evening. See page 118 for further details.

Booking form

Seating Area: please indicate number of seats required

Concert		Time	Price Code		Stalls	Loggia Boxes (8 seats)	2nd Tier Boxes (5 seats)	Choir	Balcony	Balcony (restricted view)	Car Parking	Total (£)	Office Use
1	Friday 19 July	7.30	A									:	
2	Saturday 20 July	6.00	C									:	
3	Sunday 21 July	7.30	A									:	
4	Monday 22 July	7.30	A									:	
5	Tuesday 23 July	7.30	A									:	
6	Wednesday 24 July	7.30	A					2				25:00	
7	Thursday 25 July	7.00	A	ALL-IN TICKET				2				25:00	
8	Thursday 25 July	10.00	D	ALL-IN TICKET				2				12:00	
9	Friday 26 July	7.30	A									:	
10	Saturday 27 July	7.30	A									:	
11	Sunday 28 July	7.30	A									:	
12	Monday 29 July	7.30	A									:	
13	Tuesday 30 July	7.30	A									:	
14	Wednesday 31 July	7.30	A									:	
15	Thursday 1 August	7.30	A	VOUCHER								:	
16	Friday 2 August	7.00	A	ALL-IN TICKET								:	

Arena Season half season	£80.00	FIRST HALF SECOND HALF						:
Gallery Season whole season	£80.00							:
Gallery Season half season	£45.00	FIRST HALF SECOND HALF						:
Booking Fee								1 : 25
							Total	63 : 25

Booking form

Seating Area:
please indicate number of seats required

Concert		Time	Price Code		Stalls	Loggia Boxes (8 seats)	2nd Tier Boxes (5 seats)	Choir	Balcony	Balcony (restricted view)	Car Parking	Total (£)	Office Use
1	Friday 19 July	7.30	A									:	
2	Saturday 20 July	6.00	C									:	
3	Sunday 21 July	7.30	A									:	
4	Monday 22 July	7.30	A									:	
5	Tuesday 23 July	7.30	A									:	
6	Wednesday 24 July	7.30	A									:	
7	Thursday 25 July	7.00	A	ALL-IN TICKET								:	
8	Thursday 25 July	10.00	D	ALL-IN TICKET								:	
9	Friday 26 July	7.30	A									:	
10	Saturday 27 July	7.30	A									:	
11	Sunday 28 July	7.30	A									:	
12	Monday 29 July	7.30	A									:	
13	Tuesday 30 July	7.30	A									:	
14	Wednesday 31 July	7.30	A									:	
15	Thursday 1 August	7.30	A	VOUCHER								:	
16	Friday 2 August	7.00	A	ALL-IN TICKET								:	
17	Friday 2 August	10.00	D	ALL-IN TICKET								:	
18	Saturday 3 August	7.30	B									:	
19	Sunday 4 August	4.00	D	ALL-IN TICKET								:	
20	Sunday 4 August	7.30	A	ALL-IN TICKET								:	
21	Monday 5 August	6.30	A									:	
22	Tuesday 6 August	7.30	A	VOUCHER								:	
23	Wednesday 7 August	7.00	A	VOUCHER								:	
24	Thursday 8 August	7.00	A	ALL-IN TICKET								:	
25	Thursday 8 August	10.00	D	ALL-IN TICKET								:	
26	Friday 9 August	7.30	A									:	
										Total carried over		:	

Booking form

Seating Area:
please indicate number of seats required

Concert		Time	Price Code		Stalls	Loggia Boxes (8 seats)	2nd Tier Boxes (5 seats)	Choir	Balcony	Balcony (restricted view)	Car Parking	Total (£)	Office Use
27	Saturday 10 August	7.30	Ⓐ									:	
28	Sunday 11 August	4.00	Ⓓ	ALL-IN TICKET								:	
29	Sunday 11 August	6.30	Ⓐ	ALL-IN TICKET								:	
30	Sunday 11 August	9.30	Ⓓ	ALL-IN TICKET								:	
31	Monday 12 August	7.30	Ⓐ									:	
32	Tuesday 13 August	7.30	Ⓐ	● VOUCHER								:	
33	Wednesday 14 August	7.30	Ⓐ									:	
34	Thursday 15 August	7.00	Ⓐ	ALL-IN TICKET								:	
35	Thursday 15 August	10.00	Ⓓ	ALL-IN TICKET								:	
36	Friday 16 August	7.00	Ⓑ									:	
37	Saturday 17 August	7.30	Ⓐ									:	
38	Sunday 18 August	7.30	Ⓑ									:	
39	Monday 19 August	7.30	Ⓑ									:	
40	Tuesday 20 August	7.30	Ⓑ									:	
41	Wednesday 21 August	7.30	Ⓒ									:	
42	Thursday 22 August	7.00	Ⓐ	ALL-IN TICKET								:	
43	Thursday 22 August	10.00	Ⓓ	ALL-IN TICKET								:	
44	Friday 23 August	6.30	Ⓐ									:	
45	Saturday 24 August	7.30	Ⓐ									:	
46	Sunday 25 August	7.30	Ⓐ									:	
47	Monday 26 August	11.30	Ⓐ	FULL PRICE FOR ADULTS HALF PRICE FOR UNDER 14's*								:	
48	Monday 26 August	7.00	Ⓐ									:	
49	Tuesday 27 August	7.30	Ⓐ	● VOUCHER								:	
50	Wednesday 28 August	7.30	Ⓒ									:	
51	Thursday 29 August	7.30	Ⓒ									:	
											Total carried over	:	

* NOT RESTRICTED VIEW, ARENA OR GALLERY

Booking form

Seating Area:
please indicate number of seats required

Concert		Time	Price Code		Stalls	Loggia Boxes (8 seats)	2nd Tier Boxes (5 seats)	Choir	Balcony	Balcony (restricted view)	Car Parking	Total (£)	Office Use
52	Friday 30 August	7.00	A	ALL-IN TICKET								:	
53	Friday 30 August	10.00	D	ALL-IN TICKET								:	
54	Saturday 31 August	7.30	A									:	
55	Sunday 1 September	2.30	A									:	
56	Sunday 1 September	7.30	B									:	
57	Monday 2 September	7.30	A									:	
58	Tuesday 3 September	7.00	B	ALL-IN TICKET								:	
59	Tuesday 3 September	10.00	D	ALL-IN TICKET								:	
60	Wednesday 4 Sept.	7.30	A									:	
61	Thursday 5 September	7.30	A									:	
62	Friday 6 September	7.30	A									:	
63	Saturday 7 September	8.00	A									:	
64	Sunday 8 September	7.30	A									:	
65	Monday 9 September	2.30		JUNIOR PROM TICKETS ARE NOT AVAILABLE THROUGH THE ROYAL ALBERT HALL TICKET SHOP, ALTHOUGH SEASON TICKETS ARE VALID. FOR FURTHER INFORMATION TELEPHONE 0171 765 5666 BY THE 20TH MAY									
66	Monday 9 September	7.30	A	VOUCHER								:	
67	Tuesday 10 September	7.00	A	ALL-IN TICKET								:	
68	Tuesday 10 September	10.00	D	ALL-IN TICKET								:	
69	Wednesday 11 Sept.	7.30	A									:	
70	Thursday 12 September	7.30	B									:	
71	Friday 13 September	6.45	C									:	
72	Saturday 14 September	7.30	E	THE LAST NIGHT								:	
Arena Season whole season			£130.00									:	
Arena Season half season			£80.00	FIRST HALF ☐ SECOND HALF ☐								:	
Gallery Season whole season			£80.00									:	
Gallery Season half season			£45.00	FIRST HALF ☐ SECOND HALF ☐								:	
Booking Fee												1 : 25	
											Total	:	

STAGE 5 Payment details

BLOCK CAPITALS PLEASE

Name ....

Address ....

....

....

Postcode ....

Daytime Telephone Number ....

Evening Telephone Number ....

By credit card

Please debit my Access/Visa/American Express/Mastercard account for:

£.....................

My card number is:

Expiry Date:

Signature..

Or by Cheque

☐ I enclose a cheque made payable to the Royal Albert Hall. Please leave cheques open, with an upper limit.

☐ Premiere Vouchers enclosed.

☐ Season Ticket photographs enclosed.

☐ Do not send lower priced tickets.

Please remember to enclose two passport sized photographs with season ticket applications.

Please note that a charge of £1.25 per booking will be added to cover postage and administration. When making your booking, you will automatically be sent a personal account number to link in with our new computerised system. Please quote this number in all future transactions. Tickets will be delivered within 28 days.

Return your form to: **BBC Proms Ticket Shop, Royal Albert Hall, London SW7 2AP**

Each voucher on page 114, overleaf, entitles the bearer to £3.00 off any number and any price of tickets (except Promenade or Restricted View) for the six Proms listed.

All the concerts chosen contain London, UK or world premieres.

To claim your discount, send the voucher (one for each concert) with your booking form, making the appropriate deduction of £3.00 per ticket from the total.

Or present your voucher at the Royal Albert Hall Ticket Shop (from 10 June) at the time of your purchase.

The offer is subject to availability.

Premiere Vouchers

Premiere Voucher

15 22 23 32 49 66 £3

This voucher entitles the bearer to **£3.00** off any number and any price of tickets (except Promenade or Restricted View) for one of the six Proms listed above.

Premiere Voucher

15 22 23 32 49 66 £3

This voucher entitles the bearer to **£3.00** off any number and any price of tickets (except Promenade or Restricted View) for one of the six Proms listed above.

Premiere Voucher

15 22 23 32 49 66 £3

This voucher entitles the bearer to **£3.00** off any number and any price of tickets (except Promenade or Restricted View) for one of the six Proms listed above.

Premiere Voucher

15 22 23 32 49 66 £3

This voucher entitles the bearer to **£3.00** off any number and any price of tickets (except Promenade or Restricted View) for one of the six Proms listed above.

---

15 Thursday 1 August
Alfred Schnittke arr. Gennady Rozhdestvensky:
Dead Souls – suite
London premiere

22 Tuesday 6 August
Sir Peter Maxwell Davies: Symphony No. 6
London premiere

23 Wednesday 7 August
Tan Dun: On Taoism & Orchestral Theatre II: Re
London premieres

32 Tuesday 13 August
Oliver Knussen: Horn Concerto
London premiere

49 Tuesday 27 August
György Kurtág: Stele
UK premiere

66 Monday 9 September
Anthony Powers: Symphony
World premiere

Options for Prommers

1: Nightly Tickets

These are available one hour before the start of each concert for two standing areas:

Arena **£3.00**
Look for the sign 'Arena Promenade Queue' at Door 2.

Gallery **£2.00**
Look for the sign 'Gallery Promenade Queue' at Door 10.

2: Season Tickets

To guarantee admission and save money, buy a season ticket

Season tickets (one per person) can be bought in the following ways:

Arena Season Tickets

Whole Season **£130.00**

Half Season **£80.00**
19 July – 18 August
plus Last Night (39 concerts)

Half Season **£80.00**
19 August – 14 September
including Last Night
(34 concerts)

Gallery Season Tickets

Whole Season **£80.00**

Half Season **£45.00**
19 July – 18 August
plus Last Night (39 concerts)

Half Season **£45.00**
19 August – 14 September
including Last Night
(34 concerts)

Please note that all full season tickets include the Junior Prom on 9 September, but all places for this concert will be in the Gallery and are subject to limited availability.
No Arena spaces are available.

A season ticket guarantees admission until 10 minutes before the concert. After that all remaining queues will be given equal priority. Season tickets are not transferable.

Please enclose two passport-sized photographs with season ticket applications.

The first 4 rows of the Arena are split between day and season tickets by a line, to allow early Prommers a reserved view-point. Season ticket holders to the right, Day ticket holders to the left. In the rest of the Arena standing is on an ad hoc basis.

The *only* seating available in the Arena is located around the fountain and is unreserved. Some fixed seats will be in place for Gallery Prommers. No other (portable) seating is allowed.

Prommers are asked to leave large items (including umbrellas) at the Door 4 cloakroom, open 15 minutes before the doors.

Last Night Tickets

Each purchaser buying tickets for at least SIX other concerts in the 1996 Proms season may apply for one ticket in the same price range for the Last Night.

For example
If you purchase one ticket in the Choir for six concerts, you are entitled to apply for one ticket in the Choir for the Last Night. If you purchase two tickets in the Stalls for six concerts, you are entitled to apply for two tickets in the Stalls for the Last Night.

However, each applicant is only allowed a maximum of two Last Night Tickets.

For example
If you purchase five tickets in the Balcony for six concerts, you are entitled to apply for two tickets only in the Balcony for the Last Night.

If you book tickets for at least six concerts but in different seating areas, you will be allocated seats in the area of the majority of your bookings unless otherwise directed by you that lower-priced tickets are required.

If the Last Night is sold out by the time your application is dealt with, no refunds for other tickets purchased will be payable.

To gain even more from your visit to the Proms, we have produced an All-In Ticket to encourage you, on some days when more than one concert is taking place, to linger in the Hall and enjoy an extra concert.

All-In Tickets allow a £2.00 discount on some afternoon and Late Night Concerts, provided tickets for these are purchased at the same time as tickets for the main evening concert on the same day.

All-In Tickets are not available for Arena and Gallery.

If you buy an All-In Ticket, you may not have the same seat for the different concerts but we will try to seat you in the same seating area.

Example

						Stalls	Balcony	Choir	Balcony (restricted view)	Total
34	Thursday 15 August	7.00	A		ALL-IN TICKET			1		£12.50
35	Thursday 15 August	10.00	D		ALL-IN TICKET			1		£6.00
								Total carried over		£18.50

At the Proms

Performance Time

Most concerts begin at 7.30pm, but please check individual concert dates for accurate information. Doors open three-quarters of an hour before each concert. On days when there are two concerts, there may be a slight delay in the opening of doors for the second concert.

Late Arrivals

Latecomers will not be admitted into the Hall unless or until there is a suitable break in the music.

Amenities

Ladies' Rooms are located at Door 5. Men's Rooms are located at Door 9. Hats and Coats may be left in the cloakroom at Door 4.

Dining and Refreshments

Both the Elgar Room (Door 8) and the Victoria Restaurant (Door 5) on the Balcony level are open for meals two hours prior to each concert and can be booked in advance. Less formal dining can be found in the Prince Consort Restaurant, through Doors 13/14. Bars are located on every floor. For further details see the Letheby & Christopher advertisement on page 121 or call 0171 589 8900.

Inside the Hall

Hand-luggage larger than a briefcase, folding chairs and food and drink are not allowed into the Hall. There is no smoking inside the auditorium, and cameras, tape-recorders and video cameras are not permitted.

Bringing your Children to the Proms

Children are welcome at the Proms but in consideration of our audience and performers, children under the age of five are not allowed in the auditorium. The management reserves the right to refuse admission.

Programmes

Available at various points around the Hall.

Merchandise

A selection of BBC Proms merchandise will be on sale in the Foyer at Door 6.

Broadcasting

All concerts are broadcast live on BBC Radio 3 and some will be shown on BBC Television. Please bear in mind the need for silence during the performance and show consideration for the musicians, fellow concert-goers and listeners at home by putting your hand over your mouth if you need to cough and by turning off your watch alarms. Please do not bring mobile phones into the auditorium.

Car Parking

A limited number of car park spaces are available at Imperial College (entrance in Prince Consort Road) for £5.00. Just tick the column on the booking form when applying for your tickets. Car parking is only available for evening concerts and access is from 6.00pm.

Concert-goers with special needs

The Royal Albert Hall has up to 22 spaces to reserve for concert-goers in wheelchairs. Entrance is via Doors 13/14. Phone the Ticket Shop on 0171 589 3203 ext. 2670.

An infra-red sound enhancement system is available for the hard of hearing. Receivers may be obtained free of charge from the Information Desk at Door 6.

Unaccompanied visually impaired concert-goers wishing to promenade in the Arena or Gallery should phone the Front of House Manager on 0171 589 3203 ext. 2404 in advance.

Passenger lifts can be found off the ground floor corridor at Doors 2, 8 and 11.

Special needs

How to get there

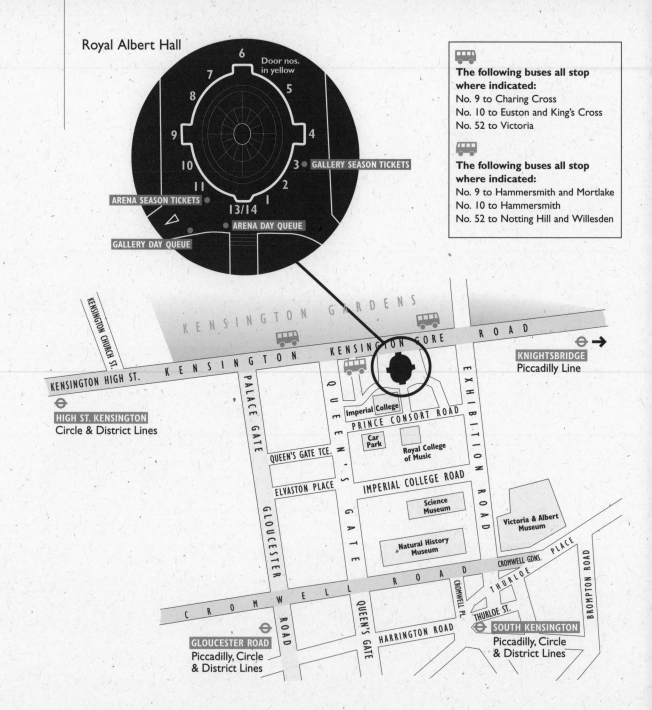

Royal Albert Hall

Door nos. in yellow

6
7
8
5
9
4
10
3 ● GALLERY SEASON TICKETS
11
2
ARENA SEASON TICKETS
13/14
1
ARENA DAY QUEUE
GALLERY DAY QUEUE

The following buses all stop where indicated:
No. 9 to Charing Cross
No. 10 to Euston and King's Cross
No. 52 to Victoria

The following buses all stop where indicated:
No. 9 to Hammersmith and Mortlake
No. 10 to Hammersmith
No. 52 to Notting Hill and Willesden

KENSINGTON GARDENS

KENSINGTON GORE ROAD

KENSINGTON CHURCH ST.

KENSINGTON HIGH ST.

KNIGHTSBRIDGE
Piccadilly Line

HIGH ST. KENSINGTON
Circle & District Lines

Imperial College

PRINCE CONSORT ROAD

PALACE GATE

QUEEN'S GATE

EXHIBITION ROAD

Car Park

Royal College of Music

QUEEN'S GATE TCE.

ELVASTON PLACE

IMPERIAL COLLEGE ROAD

GLOUCESTER ROAD

Science Museum

Natural History Museum

Victoria & Albert Museum

CROMWELL GDNS.

PLACE

CROMWELL ROAD

CROMWELL PL.

THURLOE

BROMPTON ROAD

GLOUCESTER ROAD
Piccadilly, Circle & District Lines

QUEEN'S GATE

HARRINGTON ROAD

THURLOE ST.

SOUTH KENSINGTON
Piccadilly, Circle & District Lines

"Catering of note"

Letheby & Christopher is proud to be the chosen caterer for the Royal Albert Hall.

As the Proms combines traditional classical music with new works, so we have combined classical eating and drinking with some new ideas.

The three restaurants are now open 2 hours before each performance to enable you to dine in comfort, whilst the bars offer a comprehensive range of drinks, from a glass of champagne to an excellent cup of tea.

We have also introduced new standards of service, dealing with your orders quickly, efficiently and courteously - we hope you enjoy our performance.

The Restaurants

On the Balcony level you will find the **Elgar Restaurant** offering the finest quality a la carte menu.

Also at Balcony level is the **Victoria Restaurant** offering lighter dining which, for the Proms season reflects the delights of Summer eating.

The **Prince Consort Restaurant** is at Grand Tier level and provides a range of options from a delicious light snack to a full three course meal.

The Bars

Bars are located at all levels and offer both alcoholic and non-alcoholic drinks as well as a choice of sandwiches, confectionery and ice cream.

Interval Orders

All Bars together with the Prince Consort Room are open during the interval and for speed and convenience drinks may be ordered in advance.

Box Hospitality

If you book a box for the performance you will receive details of our Box Hospitality Service, enabling you to order in advance from a comprehensive menu and bar tariff. Your order will be pre-delivered to your box.

Private Function Rooms

The Royal Albert Hall offers a choice of Private Rooms which, combined with the excellent catering and service of Letheby & Christopher, provide a unique venue for almost any corporate or private function.

For details of our Private Function service or to make a Restaurant reservation, please call the **Letheby & Christopher office at the Royal Albert Hall on 0171 589 8900.**

Please note that only food and drink purchased at the Royal Albert Hall may be consumed on the premises.

LETHEBY & CHRISTOPHER
CATERING MADE SPECIAL

TOWER
RECORDS · VIDEO · BOOKS

So much to hear, so little time, so why not start now? If you can't make it into the store, please call our Mail Order service on (0171) 287 1510 or fax (0171) 434 2766. All major credit cards accepted.

classical

A single note can be played in so many ways, and heard in so many more, that a lifetime of listening can never be enough to sample Tower's classical selection.

Diversity is the key at Tower

Here you'll find a richer, more varied range of classical recordings than any other store can offer and our friendly, knowledgeable staff are always on hand to help.

PICCADILLY
0171 439 2500

KINGSTON
0181 546 2500

KENSINGTON
0171 938 3511

BAYSWATER
0171 229 4550

GLASGOW
0141 204 2500

DUBLIN
01 671 3250

Around the Proms

Pre-Prom Talks and Events

at the Royal College of Music

Each year composers, conductors and experts introduce new and rare works at the Proms at informal Pre-Prom Talks with free admission. Additionally, education and workshop events bring the work of the BBC Orchestras to a wider audience.

Sat 20 July	Talk by Charles Osborne	4.45pm
Sun 21 July	Talk by David Drew	6.15pm
Mon 22 July	Talk by Dominic Muldowney	6.15pm

Tue 23 July	BBC Philharmonic percussion workshop	NB 11.00am
	Talk by Hans Werner Henze	6.15pm
Thu 25 July	Talk by Berthold Goldschmidt	5.45pm
Sun 28 July	BBC SO presentation and performance (with RCM wind students)	6.00pm

Players from the BBC Symphony Orchestra join forces with students from the Royal College of Music to perform repertoire they have been rehearsing together.

Wed 31 July	Talk by John Pickard	6.15pm
Sun 4 Aug	Talk by Leonard Slatkin	6.15pm
Tue 6 Aug	Talk by Sir Peter Maxwell Davies	6.15pm
Wed 7 Aug	Talk by Tan Dun	5.45pm

Sat 10 Aug	The Inaugural BBC Proms Lecture Stravinsky and Us	4.00pm

Professor Richard Taruskin of the University of California at Berkeley gives the first BBC Proms Lecture on Stravinsky, followed by a round-table discussion. This lecture will be broadcast on Radio 3 as part of Stravinsky Day on 11 August.

CHRIS CHRISTODOULOU MALCOLM CROWTHERS

Tue 13 Aug	Talk by Oliver Knussen	6.15pm
Wed 14 Aug	BBC SO composition project and talk by John Woolrich	6.00pm

A performance of new works written during a creative composition project based on John Woolrich's Oboe Concerto. The performance will be followed by John Woolrich talking about his new work.

Sun 25 Aug	Talk by Detlev Glanert	6.15pm
Wed 28 Aug	BBC SO Composers' Forum performance	6.00pm

Right
Elliott Carter

New works by Aidan Fisher, Joyce Bee, Tuan Koh, Kevin Mayo and Andrew Simpson, written as a result of the BBC Symphony Orchestra Composers' Forum '96, are performed by an ensemble of fourteen players from the BBC Symphony Orchestra.

Fri 30 Aug	Talk by Nicholas Maw	5.45pm
Sat 31 Aug	Talk by Mark-Anthony Turnage	6.15pm
Sat 7 Sept	BBC SO: presentation and performance (with RCM students)	6.30pm

Players from the BBC Symphony Orchestra join forces with students from the Royal College of Music to perform repertoire they have been rehearsing together. NB. This event will take place at Imperial College Students Union.

Mon 9 Sept	Talk by Anthony Powers	6.15pm
Tue 10 Sept	Talk by Sir Michael Tippett & Meirion Bowen	5.45pm

Proms Chamber Music

Britten Theatre, Royal College of Music
Mondays 1–2pm (except 26 August 2.30–3.30pm)

This is a new venture for the Proms: a series of lunchtime chamber concerts which picks up on some of the Proms themes – especially 'creation and recreation' – and Proms anniversaries, and explores them in a more intimate musical repertory. The venue for the eight weekly Proms Chamber Music concerts is close to the Royal Albert Hall: just across the road at the Royal College of Music, in the inviting setting of the Britten Theatre. Tickets are £4.00, and bookings can be made in advance through the Royal Albert Hall Ticket Shop on 0171 589 8212. Entry is free to season ticket holders, provided seats are reserved in advance through the box office. Tickets are also available at the Royal College of Music from 10.00am on the morning of each recital, subject to availability. Season ticket holders who obtain tickets from the RCM on the morning of the recital will be charged £4.00.

July 22 Arditti Quartet

Beethoven: Grosse Fuge
Elliott Carter: String Quartet No. 5
London premiere
Henri Dutilleux: Ainsi la nuit

July 29 **Philip Mead** piano

Ives: Three-Page Sonata
Copland: Variations
Barber: Piano Sonata

Aug 5 **Haffner Ensemble**
Nicholas Daniel
oboe/director
Sally Burgess
mezzo-soprano

Ravel arr. Jones:
Le Tombeau de
    Couperin
Falla: Concerto for Harpsichord and
    Five Instruments
Ravel: Three Mallarmé Poems

Aug 12 **Peter Donohoe** and **Martin Roscoe**
piano duo

Mozart arr. Grieg: Fantasia in C minor, K475
Lutoslawski: Variations on a Theme of
    Paganini
Grainger: Fantasy on Gershwin's
    'Porgy and Bess'

Aug 19 **Oslo Philharmonic Wind Soloists**

Haydn: Divertimenti a 6
Dvořák: Serenade in D minor

Aug 26 **Gould Piano Trio** (NB at 2.30pm)

Mendelssohn: Piano Trio No. 2
Clara Schumann: Piano Trio

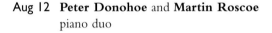

Sept 2 **Raphael Ensemble**

Wolf: Italian Serenade
Bruckner: String Quintet

Sept 9 **Joanna MacGregor** piano
Madeleine Mitchell violin
Christopher van Kampen cello
David Campbell clarinet

J. S. Bach: Contrapunctus No. 14 from
    'The Art of Fugue'
Messiaen: Quartet for the End of Time

Above
Joanna MacGregor

Far left
Haffner Ensemble

Left
Gould Piano Trio

Below left
Raphael Ensemble

PETER RAUTER NICK WHITE/COLLINS CLASSICS CATHERINE ASHMORE

Exploring the Proms on BBC Radio 3

Radio 3 offers you the complete Proms season in the comfort of your own home. Not only is every Prom broadcast live on Radio 3, but there are programmes and series designed to add background and enhance your enjoyment of the Proms.

Proms News

The lively weekly magazine programme *Proms News*, presented by Stephen Johnson, will highlight a main event and survey the concerts, including interviews with major artists and up-to-the-minute information as the season unfolds **(Saturdays, 9.00am, repeated Sundays, 30 minutes before the start of the evening's Prom)**.

Proms Documentaries

A major series of in-depth music documentaries on **Saturdays at 5.45pm** during the season gives you a chance to focus on composers featured in this year's Proms, such as Hans Werner Henze and Kurt Weill, and performers including George Malcolm and Mstislav Rostropovich.

Proms Trails scattered throughout each day of the season will keep you up-to-the-minute with all Proms events

Proms Artist of the Week

Some of the big names performing at the Proms will be featured as Proms Artists of the Week in two of Radio 3's regular programmes: *Brian Kay's Sunday Morning* **(Sundays, 9.00am–12.30pm)** and *Musical Encounters* **(Weekdays, 10.00am–12.00 noon)**.

Robert Lloyd	**14–19 July**
András Schiff	**21–26 July**
Gennady Rozhdestvensky	**28 July–2 August**
Simon Preston	**4–9 August**
Judith Howarth	**11–16 August**
Anne-Sophie Mutter	**18–23 August**
Claudio Abbado	**25–30 August**
Alfred Brendel	**1–6 September**
Daniel Barenboim	**8–13 September**

Proms Composer of the Week

During the Proms, the ever-popular *Composer of the Week* **(weekdays at 12.00 noon, repeated the next week at 11.30pm, 12.00 midnight on Fridays)** will celebrate composer anniversaries and complement some of the major themes in the Proms:

Haydn	**15–19 July**
Weill	**22–26 July**
Handel	**29 July–2 August**
Stravinsky	**5–9 August**
Beethoven	**12–16 August**
Berg	**19–23 August**
Brahms	**26–30 August**
Falla and Gerhard	**2–6 September**
Bach	**9–13 September**

You can write to the Proms at:
BBC Proms, Broadcasting House, London W1A 1AA
or send an e-mail to: **Proms@bbc.co.uk**
Visit the all-new Proms site on the internet at:
http://www.bbc.co.uk/proms/

Experience the
600 Watts of clean
power of this unique
audio visual system.
Mission M-time combines
the audiophile attributes of
a quality stereo setup with all
the facets of a state-of-the-art
home theatre installation in a
stylish enclosure that will harmoniously
blend into your living environment.

Late Night Revelry

Katina Dawe outlines the advantages of staying out late

Above
The London
Sinfonietta

Right
Dawn Upshaw sings
Americana in Prom 8

Far right
Richard Bernas (right)
conducts the
premiere of *Oceanos*
by James Dillon (left)
in Prom 53

Below
Wayne Marshall plays
Stravinsky in Prom 30

SOMEHOW AT Late Night Proms the sense of expectation is keener, the pre-concert hush more charged. There is a feeling of being out after hours, a heightened anticipation because the evening is just beginning when the rest of the world is going home.

For regular Promenaders, staying on for the Late Night Prom is an opportunity to demonstrate their stamina as they return to the Hall, leaving their less hardy companions behind at the bar. For others, it is perhaps a chance to enjoy a leisurely pre-concert meal and a summer evening stroll to the Hall as the light fades.

The first Late Night Prom took place twenty-six years ago at the Royal Albert Hall, and over the next eighteen years they featured in a number of settings, including The Round House and St Paul's, Knightsbridge, chosen to reflect the informal nature of these concerts. In 1990 they made a wholesale return to the Royal Albert Hall, where surprisingly the space and grandeur seem to make the occasion more intimate.

Late Night Proms serve as a forum for unusual and experimental programmes which often make use of

the Hall's vast spaces, as well as for smaller-scale concerts ranging from the Nash Ensemble's contribution this year to the Spanish theme, to the debut of Philippe Herreweghe's Collegium Vocale Ghent in an all-Bach programme. The 1996 season also sees a new departure, the London Sinfonietta accompanying the American soprano Dawn Upshaw in a late night recital of twentieth-century repertoire including Bernstein, Gershwin and Weill.

World musicians are no strangers to the Proms and this year will feature a concert by the Calcutta Drum Orchestra and Pandit Shivkumar Sharma. The world premiere of James Dillon's *Oceanos*, the concluding movement of his monumental *Nine Rivers* cycle, and the UK premiere of Kevin Volans's Piano Concerto will be highlights of concerts by Music Projects/London and the Netherlands Wind Ensemble, while the BBC Singers display their versatility in a programme including two pieces commissioned for their Seventieth Anniversary Season, as well as works by Britten and Victoria. There will be eight Late Night Proms in all, or nine if we include the culmination of 'Stravinsky Day', which begins at 9.30pm instead of the usual 10pm.

So next time you're considering another post-concert drink, why not instead consider a post-concert concert?

See page 117 for details of the special All-In Tickets covering two Proms on the same evening

The first hundred years
of recorded sound

The British Library National Sound Archive is one of the largest sound archives in the world. The NSA's collections include opera and music in the western concert tradition, the classical music of other traditions, as well as folk music, pop and jazz.

The Archive collects *commercial releases* from all over the world, and, through its free listening service, also provides public access to both the *BBC Sound Archives* and its own off-air recordings of

broadcasts, talks, features and documentaries about music and musicians. There is a growing collection too of TV programmes, laser discs and videos. All can now be easily identified on the NSA's new *computerised catalogue.*

The Listening Service and the Library & Information Service are open to the public from 10.00am to 5.00pm, Monday to Friday, with late opening to 9.00pm on Thursdays.

THE BRITISH LIBRARY

NATIONAL SOUND ARCHIVE

29 Exhibition Road, London SW7 2AS

Tel 0171 412 7430 (*library & information service*)
0171 412 7418 (*listening service*)
0171 412 7440 (*general enquiries*); 0171 412 7416 (*fax*)

Index of Artists

Alan Opie (baritone) 54
Tadaaki Otaka (conductor) 66
Anne Sofie von Otter (mezzo-soprano) 71

P

René Pape (bass)* 71
Andrew Parrott (conductor) 30
Libor Pešek (conductor) 34
Trevor Pinnock (conductor) 12
Artur Pizarro (piano) 34
Mary Plazas (soprano)* 2
Mikhail Pletnev (conductor*) 24, 26
Victoria Postnikova (piano) 15
Rodrigo del Pozo (haute-contre)* 25
Simon Preston (organ) 20
Christopher Purves (baritone) 48

R

Thomas Randle (tenor) 42
Sir Simon Rattle (conductor) 57, 58
Stephen Richardson (bass) 23, 29, 48
Jean Rigby (mezzo-soprano) 48
Nicolas Rivenq (bass)* 25
Martin Robertson (saxophone)* 54
Nicolas Robertson (tenor) 25
Tony Robinson (presenter)* 65
Joan Rodgers (soprano) 54
Anthony Rolfe Johnson (tenor) 48
Mstislav Rostropovich (conductor) 9
Gennady Rozhdestvensky (conductor) 15

S

Gidon Saks (bass-baritone)* 3
Esa-Pekka Salonen (conductor) 32
Roberto Scandiuzzi (bass)* 2
Michael Schade (tenor) 36
Christine Schäfer (soprano) 44
András Schiff (piano) 10
Andreas Scholl (counter-tenor)* 16, 68
Wolfgang Schöne (baritone) 1, 44
John Scott (organ) 71
Pandit Shivkumar Sharma (santoor)* 17
Teresa Shaw (mezzo-soprano)* 30
Peter Sidhom (baritone) 42

Vassily Sinaisky (conductor)* 5
Leonard Slatkin (conductor) 20
Geert Smits (baritone)* 36
Sir Georg Solti (conductor) 71
Thomas Stacy (cor anglais)* 40
Markus Stenz (conductor) 3
Pamela Helen Stephen (mezzo-soprano) 48
Eric Stern (conductor)* 8

T

Tan Dun (conductor) 23
James Taylor (tenor)* 68
Robert Tear (tenor) 29
Bryn Terfel (baritone) 48
Christian Tetzlaff (violin) 7
Jean-Yves Thibaudet (piano) 69
Alexander Toradze (piano) 62
Yan Pascal Tortelier (conductor) 4, 60, 69
Mark Tucker (tenor) 48
Barry Tuckwell (horn) 32

U

Dawn Upshaw (soprano) 8

V

Osmo Vänskä (conductor) 46
Jonathan Veira (baritone)* 44
Lars Vogt (piano) 23
Deborah Voigt (soprano) 71

W

John Wallace (trumpet) 72
Günter Wand (conductor) 61
Janice Watson (soprano) 48
Willard White (bass) 21
Mark Wigglesworth (conductor) 13, 14
John Williams (guitar) 31
David Wilson-Johnson (bass-baritone) 29
James Wood (conductor) 29
Barry Wordsworth (conductor) 45
Catrin Wyn-Davies (soprano)* 3
Catherine Wyn-Rogers (mezzo-soprano) 12, 42

Z

Heinz Zednik (tenor)* 3
Thomas Zehetmair (violin) 55

GROUPS

Les Arts Florissants 21
BBC Concert Orchestra 45, 65
BBC National Chorus of Wales 48
BBC National Orchestra of Wales 13, 14, 48, 64, 66
BBC Philharmonic 4, 5, 60, 69
BBC Scottish Symphony Orchestra 23, 46, 47
BBC Singers 11, 31, 49, 59, 71, 72
BBC Symphony Chorus 1, 11, 31, 37, 51, 54, 72
BBC Symphony Orchestra 1, 6, 11, 15, 20, 29, 33, 37, 42, 49, 54, 61, 67, 72
Berlin Philharmonic Orchestra 50, 51
Birmingham Contemporary Music Group 28, 30
Members of Birmingham Royal Ballet* 28
Bournemouth Symphony Orchestra 7
Calcutta Drum Orchestra* 17
Chamber Orchestra of Europe 56
Chicago Symphony Orchestra 70, 71
City of Birmingham Symphony Orchestra 57, 58
Chorus and Orchestra of Collegium Vocale, Ghent* 68
English Chamber Orchestra 10
The English Concert 12
Choir of The English Concert 12
European Union Youth Orchestra 18
Glyndebourne Festival Opera 44
Joven Orquesta Nacional de España* 31
London Adventist Chorale 19
The London Philharmonic 44, 52
London Sinfonietta 3, 8
London Sinfonietta Chorus 3
London Symphony Chorus 48, 51
London Symphony Orchestra 9
London Voices 71

Monteverdi Choir 36
Music Projects/London* 53
Nash Ensemble 35
National Youth Orchestra of Great Britain 27
Netherlands Wind Ensemble* 43
Choir of New College, Oxford 16
New London Chamber Choir 29
New London Children's Choir 65
New York Philharmonic 40, 41
Orchestra of the Age of Enlightenment 16
Orchestra of the Eighteenth Century* 55
Orchestre Révolutionnaire et Romantique 36
Oslo Philharmonic Orchestra 38, 39
Philharmonia Chorus 42
Philharmonia Orchestra 32
Polyphony 53
Rotterdam Philharmonic Orchestra 62, 63
Royal Liverpool Philharmonic Orchestra 34
Royal Opera Chorus 2
Orchestra of The Royal Opera House 2
Royal Philharmonic Orchestra 22
Russian National Orchestra* 24, 26
St James's Baroque Players 25
St James's Singers 25
Taverner Choir 30
Winchester Cathedral Choir 16

* First appearance at a BBC Henry Wood Promenade Concert

Index of Works

Wiltshire Youth Orchestra

WAGNER
Siegfried *Act 1*

Siegfried: **Stephen O'Mara**

Mime: **John Harris**   The Wanderer: **Sir Donald McIntyre**

Conductor: **Lionel Friend**

Royal College of Music, London
Tuesday 27 August 7.30pm
Tickets & information: 01225 753175

City Hall, Salisbury
Wednesday 28 August 7.30pm
Tickets & information: 01722 327676

Symphony Hall, Birmingham
Saturday 31 August 7.30pm
Tickets & information: 0121 212 3333

In association with

Wiltshire COUNTY COUNCIL   **RoadChef**   THE NATIONAL HERITAGE ARTS SPONSORSHIP SCHEME

Index of Advertisers

1 JOANNA LUMLEY
Elgar
Pomp and Circumstance
March No. 1 in D major
BBC Symphony Orchestra
Andrew Davis conductor
Prom 72

Mahler
Symphony No. 2 in C minor
'Resurrection'
BBC Philharmonic
Sir Charles Mackerras
conductor
Prom 51

Gershwin
An American in Paris
BBC Philharmonic
Yan Pascal Tortelier conductor
Prom 27

Britten
Four Sea-Interludes from
'Peter Grimes'
BBC Philharmonic
Yan Pascal Tortelier conductor
Prom 9

Traditional arr. Ken Burton
Swing Down, Sweet Chariot
London Adventist Chorale
Ken Burton conductor
Prom 19

Indian Drumming
Latif Ahmed Khan tabla
Prom 17

Gershwin
'But not for me' from
'Girl Crazy'
BBC Concert Orchestra
Robert Ziegler conductor
Prom 27

Mark-Anthony Turnage
Your Rockaby
BBC Symphony Orchestra
Andrew Davis conductor
Martin Robertson saxophone
Prom 54

3 JAMES NAUGHTIE
Verdi
Don Carlos
BBC National Orchestra
of Wales
David Pryce Jones conductor
Gwynne Howell bass
Prom 2

2 JEREMY PAXMAN
Rakhmaninov
Rhapsody on a Theme of
Paganini
BBC Scottish Symphony
Orchestra
Jerzy Maksymiuk conductor
Stephen Hough piano
Prom 5

Schumann
Piano Concerto in A minor
BBC Symphony Orchestra
Gennady Rozhdestvensky
conductor
Victoria Postnikova piano
Prom 23

Berg
Lulu
BBC Symphony Orchestra
Andrew Davis conductor
Patricia Wise soprano
Prom 44

Mendelssohn
Piano Trio No. 2 in C minor
Joachim Piano Trio:
Rebecca Hirsch violin
Caroline Dearnley cello
John Lenehan piano
Proms Chamber Music
26 August

Beethoven
Symphony No. 9
in D minor 'Choral'
BBC National Orchestra
of Wales
BBC National Chorus
of Wales
BBC Symphony Chorus
Tadaaki Otaka conductor
Prom 71

CD Prom 96

This specially produced CD features favourite
extracts – chosen and introduced by our
celebrity guests – from a range of music being
played in this year's Proms. Most of the
recordings were made live by the BBC and
feature the BBC's own orchestras. © BBC 1996

Andrew Davis appears by courtesy of Teldec
Classics International GmbH

Recorded on location and in the BBC studios,
Broadcasting House, February/March 1996.
Engineers: Philip Ashley and Lyndon Jones
Producer: Edward Blakeman

4 NED SHERRIN
Britten
Four Sea-Interludes from
'Peter Grimes'
BBC Philharmonic
Yan Pascal Tortelier conductor
Prom 9

6 RICHARD STILGOE
Brahms
Piano Concerto No. 2
in B flat major
BBC Philharmonic
Yan Pascal Tortelier conductor
Prom 13

9 RORY BREMNER
Berlioz
Symphonie fantastique
BBC Symphony Orchestra
Andrew Davis conductor
Prom 34

10 SIR DAVID PUTTNAM
Beethoven
Leonore
BBC Scottish Symphony Orchestra
Jerzy Maksymiuk conductor
Prom 36

5 RICHARD WILSON
Beethoven
Symphony No. 7 in A ma[jor]
BBC Symphony Orchest[ra]
Andrew Davis conducto[r]
Prom 11

7 PRUNELLA SCALES
Handel
Semele
Yorkshire Baroque Soloist[s]
Peter Seymour conductor
Gillian Fisher soprano
Prom 21

8 PAUL McCARTNEY
Rodrigo
Concierto de Aranjuez
BBC Scottish Symphony
Orchestra
Jerzy Maksymiuk
conductor
Carlos Bonell guitar
Prom 31